HOW TO
SUCCESSFULLY WITH

ANXIETY AND DEPRESSION

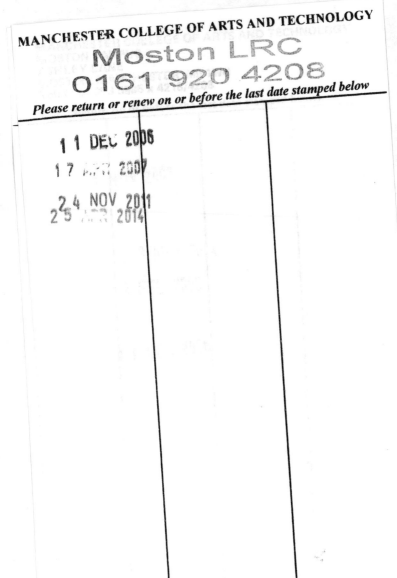

MANCHESTER COLLEGE OF ARTS AND TECHNOLOGY

Moston LRC
0161 920 4208

Please return or renew on or before the last date stamped below

First published in Great Britain in 2001 by
Wellhouse Publishing Ltd
31 Middle Bourne Lane
Lower Bourne
Farnham
Surrey GU10 3NH

DISCLAIMER

The aim of this book is to provide general information only and
should not be treated as a substitute for the medical advice of
your doctor or any other health care professional. The publisher
and author is not responsible or liable for any diagnosis made by
a reader based on the contents of this book. Always consult your
doctor if you are in any way concerned about your health.

A catalogue record for this book is available from the British Library

ISBN 1 903784 03 4

Printed and bound in Great Britain by
Biddles Ltd., Surrey. www.biddles.co.uk

For Denis with all my love

Acknowledgements

My warmest thanks are due to the following who made this book a pleasure to write. My agent Teresa Chris proved to be her usual source of practical and moral support, while Brian Keen and Barbara Vesey at Wellhouse Publishing made the day-to-day experience of writing this book as enjoyable as possible. My very special thanks go to Dr Nicola Green who took great pains to read the manuscript, and provided suggestions that were both perceptive and always constructive. My patients also receive my gratitude for teaching me about the reality of anxiety and depression. Last, but never least, my love as always to my husband Denis who is always such a source of support and understanding when the pressure is on.

Contents

Chapter 5 : Complementary and Alternative Treatments

Chapter 6 : Nutritional Self-help

Chapter 7 : Herbs, Homeopathy and Aromatherapy

Chapter 8 : Lifestyle Changes

Chapter 9 : Advice for Carers

Introduction

It is undeniably true that we live in stressful times. Many of us have to cope on a daily basis with a variety of different pressures that may include financial worries, emotional stresses, bereavement, the break-up of close and intimate relationships, and insecurity at work. When we are feeling well and resilient we are likely to be able to cope with a wide range of these stressful factors and maintain a reasonable level of emotional equilibrium.

However, if we become mentally and emotionally overloaded at a vulnerable phase of our lives, we may find that we begin to suffer from symptoms of anxiety and/or depression. This may also occur more readily in those of us who have a family or personal history of these two common conditions.

Although the symptoms of anxiety and depression can be extremely distressing, debilitating and disruptive, it helps to bear in mind that these conditions can also be an important way of making us stop and take stock of the quality of our lives. If we have been pushing ourselves too hard mentally, emotionally and physically, experiencing the symptoms of emotional illness can force us to take action to improve our mental and emotional health.

When Are We Especially Vulnerable?

There are particular times of life and major life events that can make us more vulnerable to experiencing a combination of anxiety and depression. These may include any of the following:

- during and after pregnancy
- during the menopause
- after the diagnosis of a major illness
- bereavement
- separation and divorce
- redundancy and other financial disasters
- nursing and caring for a close relative over an extended period of time
- any major change or upheaval in life circumstances

It is sometimes the cumulative nature of these events that may be the triggering factor. In other words, some people may find that they cope very well with the pressures of a busy working life and demanding relationship until they become ill or suffer a bereavement, when they may find that things just get too much to handle.

On the other hand, those who have a past history of anxiety and depression or close family members who have suffered from the same problem may need no more than one of these factors to trigger a depressive or anxious episode.

It also bears remembering that there is a broad spectrum of potential experience of anxiety and depression. Some people may experience mild, fairly short-lived episodes of these problems that they can handle by themselves once they understand why the symptoms are there and what they can do to support themselves through the phases of emotional upheaval.

Others may find that they move into a state of severe clinical anxiety and depression that leaves them feeling frightened, lost, disoriented and unable to cope with the regular demands that they need to meet their day-to-day lives. This is a situation where professional guidance, reassurance and support are needed, so that the sufferers understand that they are not alone in suffering in this way (feeling isolated can be one of the most alarming aspects of depression).

In addition, once support is at hand in the form of professional medical help such as medication, cognitive therapy or psychotherapeutic approaches, sufferers are likely to feel a huge sense of relief that something positive and practical can be done to support them through a very traumatic experience. This is especially important, since despair can set in when people feel there is no possible way out of their problems. Feeling that practical options for change are available can make all the difference in such a situation.

Why Anxiety And Depression Often Occur Together

Although symptoms of anxiety can be quite different from depressive symptoms, it is also true that they can frequently overlap. This is sometimes due to the fact that when someone is depressed, they are aware that they are genuinely at risk of losing aspects of their lives that are essential to them. Features of life that can feel threatened may include intimate relationships, jobs, religious faith, a sense of meaning in life, identity or financial security. If someone feels threatened in any of these ways, there is a good chance that they are likely to feel acute anxiety at times.

It is also true that some symptoms of anxiety can echo those of depression. These may include any of the following: disturbed sleep pattern, poor concentration, lack of or lowered libido, digestive upsets, headaches, aches and pains and lack of energy.

It can help enormously to realize that there is a wide range of practical measures that can provide positive support in dealing with symptoms of anxiety and depression. Since feeling powerless is one of the most frightening aspects of these illnesses, positive strategies for moving towards recovery have a particularly significant role to play. These measures embrace conventional and alternative medical support, as well as nutritional, psychological and exercise hints for self-help. It is the purpose of this book to give a basic overview of these essential tools of support.

Chapter One

Understanding Anxiety

The word *anxiety* can cover an extremely wide spectrum of symptoms, of varying intensity. There can be very few of us who do not recognize the flutter of 'butterflies' in the stomach at the anticipation of a coming stressful event. Although this can be regarded as a form of anxiety, it is very often the positive trigger that gives us the 'edge' we need in order to cope more effectively with whatever stress we are exposed to. This is, of course, provided it doesn't escalate into a more severe nervous state, which can have a counterproductive effect on our ability to react effectively and appropriately.

It is perfectly natural to feel tense and nervous in response to the pressure of a stressful, demanding situation, but those who suffer from chronic anxiety are likely to feel dismay at experiencing unpleasant symptoms of emotional, mental and physical tension and unease for the most trivial of reasons. Common features of chronic anxiety can include irrational phobias or full-blown panic attacks that may descend out of the blue, with no obvious trigger being present.

As explained in the Introduction, it is very common for anxiety and depression to emerge as flip sides of the same coin. In such a situation, if treatment is to have the maximum positive impact it must address both conditions equally well.

The good news, however, is that there are effective ways of dealing with anxiety symptoms that empower those affected to feel able to take some control into their own hands. If anxiety symptoms are severe, well-established, or arise in combination with depressive problems, effective self-help strategies are going to yield the best results when used in combination with the support of professional help. In this way sufferers are likely to feel that while expert help is on hand when the going gets rough, they are not limited to taking a passive stance with regard to their own mental, emotional and physical health.

Some people may be anxious by nature, and feel there must be something wrong if there is nothing to feel worried or anxious about. Others, however, may previously have been quite laid back but find that specific life events have set off a tendency to persistent, low-grade anxiety symptoms. There are several possible triggers.

Excessive Stress

Anxiety symptoms frequently raise their head when stress levels are not being adequately managed. The characteristic symptoms of anxiety listed below (see page 14) commonly emerge when people feel at the mercy of an overwhelming stress load, which can make them feel out of control and lacking in self-esteem. The negative stress load may be generated at work, where they may feel they are expected to reach unrealistic targets or excessively punishing schedules. On the other hand, some people may feel quite in command in a professional setting, but find that their domestic environment causes a different kind of stress through lack of communication or constant bickering. If this is unacknowledged they may begin to experience symptoms of anxiety and/or depression.

Receiving a Shock or Bad News

Problems with anxiety may emerge some time after an accident (such as a severe fall, especially in the elderly), witnessing an accident, or after distressing news such as a bereavement, being told of the termination of a relationship, or loss of a job. Even if you feel you are coping reasonably well at the time, you may find that anxiety symptoms emerge some time later as a delayed reaction. This is due to the way in which you may be in shock when initially responding to the upsetting situation, with the result that natural feelings of distress and anxiety may be temporarily suppressed. As a result, you may be surprised at first to find yourself feeling afraid and tense in a situation where there is no identifiable reason for feeling so upset.

Going Through a Negative or Traumatic Experience of Childbirth

Experiencing childbirth can be one of the situations that makes a woman feel especially vulnerable and alone. This sensation can be made even more intense if she has had unrealistically high expectations, but has found that the reality bears little resemblance to what she may have hoped for. This may be due to unforeseen medical complications, inadequate pain relief or a long, arduous labour. The overall effect of any combination of these potential problems may leave a woman with very little confidence in her body, and a general sense of 'falling apart' in the immediate period after childbirth. If it is a first baby a general sense of anxiety may be compounded by a strong sense of feeling ill-equipped to deal with the multiple, sometimes unforeseen needs of a young baby. Anxiety symptoms may also be exaggerated by a general sense of emotional, mental and physical tiredness that can emerge in the early months of looking after a baby due to lack of sleep. This can be compounded further by having other young children to look after.

The Menopause
Some women may find that they experience severe anxiety symptoms for the first time in their lives as they approach and move through menopause. Feelings bordering on panic may accompany or precede hot flushes or night sweats, or women may find that they suddenly can't tolerate being in narrow, crowded or closed-in environments. Apart from the hormonal fluctuations that occur leading up to and during menopause, problems such as emerging anxiety and depression may also be linked to expectations women have about ageing and obvious signs of change that begin to appear in their faces and bodies at this time. Provided women understand what is happening, once they have accomplished this major transitional phase and moved beyond menopause, there is a good chance that sensations of anxiety may disappear with the hot flushes and night sweats. However, if symptoms prove more persistent, extra help may be obtained from an alternative medical source which may benefit menopausal as well as anxiety symptoms.

For additional triggers that may influence the emergence of anxiety symptoms, see page 22, where triggers of depression are discussed. Symptoms of anxiety and depression have a marked tendency to overlap.

This section talks about some common and characteristic features of anxiety. However, as you shall discover from the short case histories that follow, different symptoms emerge with different rates of intensity in each individual. Some common symptoms may not appear at all, while other, less expected features may be particularly marked. Alternative therapists are especially aware of this emphasis on the individuality of each patient, since most therapies with a holistic perspective work from the understanding that it is a person being treated, not just disease symptoms in isolation.

Predictable anxiety symptoms may include any of the following:
- hyperventilation (breathing rapidly and in a shallow way from the upper chest)
- pain, or a sense of constriction and tightness in the chest
- feeling hot and bothered and sweaty, or cold and clammy
- palpitations (an unpleasant awareness of a rapid or irregular heartbeat)
- nausea and/or recurrent indigestion
- lack of appetite
- diarrhoea
- cramping pains in the stomach and abdomen
- trembling, weak sensations in the muscles
- dry mouth
- dizziness and light-headedness
- poor memory and lack of concentration
- a powerful sense of impending terror or panic
- unsatisfactory and unrefreshing sleep pattern and sleep quality
- recurrent tension headaches
- extreme mental, emotional, and physical fatigue

Bruce's Story
Bruce's life had been largely fine until he was given a promotion at work. This was generally good news for him, but unfortunately brought with it an added pressure that he was finding increasingly difficult to handle. His new job involved giving regular presentations, which were getting increasingly difficult for him to do. A visit to his doctor had resulted in a prescription of beta-blockers, which Bruce

was advised to take before giving his presentations. Although these took the edge off his symptoms, he was still experiencing an increasing amount of distress, and he felt his rising sense of panic and fear was becoming obvious to his audience.

By the time Bruce came to see me he had tried relaxation techniques, hypnotherapy and aromatherapy, with no marked relief in his symptoms, which now included a rising sense of nausea and panic whenever he was faced with public speaking, which resulted in his being drenched in a cold, clammy sweat. His heart would feel as though it was racing and his palms would become very sweaty. Bruce felt he needed to face up to this new responsibility, while his irrational terror and panic was pulling him in the opposite direction. This led to his feeling an overwhelming desire to 'cut and run' away from the source of stress as fast as possible. Logically he knew he could do the presentations very well, which made him feel even worse about the unreasonable quality of his panic and anxiety.

The first homoeopathic remedy that Bruce was given did little to alleviate his ability to cope in a stressful situation, but the second (Lycopodium) promoted a dramatic improvement. He claimed that he had dealt with his latest presentation more effectively than he had been able to do for years. In fact, after the presentation was over he felt on an emotional 'high'. All that Bruce needed from this point was a dose of his homoeopathic remedy before a presentation if he felt any sense of panic developing, and he would sail through it. He was able to dispense with his beta-blockers after his second month of homoeopathic treatment.

Amy's Story

Amy's personality had always tended towards tense and anxious, but matters reached a serious stage during her first pregnancy. Her health was not good from the first month, with recurrent bladder and kidney infections providing a worrying feature. In addition, she experienced recurrent bouts of vaginal thrush, which added to her physical discomfort and general feeling of being run-down.

Amy suffered frequent bouts of light-headedness during her pregnancy, which led to her developing a significant fear of fainting. This never actually happened, but the constant dread of it led to acute panic attacks for a year and a half after Amy's baby was born. The severity of these panic attacks was severely hampering Amy's life, as she developed an unmanageable fear of going out for a walk on her own, even for short distances. Previously someone who enjoyed the company of her friends, Amy found she was becoming an unwilling prisoner in her own home.

Amy would know a panic attack was going to develop by the tell-tale sign of a hot sweat. The frightening sense of light-headedness would shortly follow, with hyperventilation and a sense of being unable to move an inch for fear of falling. The dizziness would feel very much worse for standing, and would be slightly eased by sitting still.

Amy was aware that she had extremely low blood pressure, and suspected that she might be experiencing low blood sugar levels if she didn't make a point of eating small amounts regularly. This would lead to unpleasant sensations of trembling in her arms and legs, as well an increased sense of dizziness and disorientation.

In addition, Amy had a history of problems with pre-menstrual mood swings and headaches that had led her, in the past, to experiencing severe bouts of uncontrollable weeping and irritability. These had also become very much worse after her pregnancy, and were accompanied by a profound sense of mental, emotional and physical exhaustion. The latter was made even more problematic by the disturbed quality of sleep Amy had experienced since the birth of her baby. Even though her daughter's sleep pattern had settled into a reasonable routine, and her partner would share getting up during the night, Amy found that she would constantly wake at 2 a.m., her mind racing and anxious.

By the time of her first homoeopathic consultation, Amy felt that conventional medication had been unable to relieve her situation. We discussed dietary ways of easing the symptoms linked to unstable blood sugar levels, and considered foods and drinks that might aggravate feelings of tension and anxiety, and those that would have a more calming, mood-balancing effect. In addition, Amy was given a form of the homoeopathic remedy Sepia to take on a daily basis. This is a frequently prescribed homoeopathic remedy which can ease the symptoms of overwhelming exhaustion, anxiety, irritability or apathy that follow childbirth. For the past four months Amy has been free of panic attacks, and she has, to her delight, begun to resume a normal social life, casually going shopping in public places – something that had become impossible for her to handle while she was so acutely fearful and anxious. As Amy's energy levels have improved, so has her confidence.

Pam's Story

Pam's problems came sharply to the fore on a family holiday to Greece. Although she had had a general tendency to feel bouts of anxiety in the past, the focus of her extreme fear centred around the safety of her child. Issues surrounding the security of this child had been apparent since he was born, with Pam revealing during the course of her homoeopathic treatment that she had a lingering, irrational fear of doing him, or her partner, harm of some kind. Pam developed a powerful phobia of knives and other sharp objects as a result of her underlying fear of any harm being sustained by those she loved most.

Pam presented with a general sense of insecurity which revealed itself in bouts of jealousy, weepiness and extreme irritability. However, her overwhelming problem was linked to feeling a general sense of foreboding about what was about to happen, with a powerful sensation of anxiety settling like a knot in her stomach. Her whole digestive tract could feel so disordered and tense that it would feel a huge effort at times even to swallow. Hand in hand with this digestive uneasiness went a craving for sweet things and tea.

Pam was very dismayed at the change in herself, since she had generally regarded herself as a basically independent, resilient person before suffering these severe attacks of unreasonable insecurity and fear. She had had a tendency in the past to keep her emotions to herself, needing quite a bit of emotional space and privacy.

Not surprisingly, Pam's sleep pattern had become erratic and disordered, with a corresponding sense of feeling tired all the time. It was also predictable that Pam suffered from tension headaches on a regular basis, which would make her feel very sick and unwell.

Fortunately, as Pam came to see me she was also seeing a clinical psychologist, which she was finding helpful. We talked about relaxation techniques and the importance of learning how to breathe from the area of the diaphragm, in order to induce a more tranquil, less anxious state of mind. In addition, Pam received a prescription of the homoeopathic remedy Arsenicum album, which she took each day for the first six months of treatment. Over this period of time Pam's anxiety attacks diminished greatly in frequency and severity, while her sleep pattern also improved enormously. As a result, her energy levels returned to normal. After a year of treatment Pam was anxiety-attack free, and she remained so until three months ago when she required a brief course of top-up treatment.

Related Physical Problems

Although anxiety is primarily a state of mind, it is a condition that can have a powerful effect on our bodies, giving rise to a host of physical symptoms.

Irritable Bowel Syndrome (IBS)

The diagnosis of irritable bowel syndrome is often made by ruling out other potential problems through conducting a range of tests such as endoscopy, barium enema, sigmoidoscopy, and ultrasound imaging. If these investigations do not reveal the presence of a stomach ulcer, Crohn's disease, gall bladder disease, or a tumour in the stomach or bowel, there is a good chance that IBS will be diagnosed. The symptoms include recurrent indigestion, heartburn, nausea, lack of appetite, cramping pains, and alternation between diarrhoea and constipation.

While certain physical factors can undoubtedly aggravate problems with IBS (such as too little, or excessive amounts of, fibre in the diet, or food sensitivities to dairy products, sugar or wheat), being overly stressed and anxious also appears to play a major role in this chronic condition.

Some sufferers may have a clue to how this happens if they have experienced feeling sick and having severe bouts of diarrhoea before a stressful event, such as speaking in public or sitting an important exam. If they are generally fairly easy-going by nature, these symptoms should disappear as soon as the focus of the anticipatory stress and anxiety has gone. However, those who suffer from IBS are likely to experience low-grade versions of these symptoms on a recurrent basis, especially if they have not discovered adequate stress-management techniques in order to ease the burden of on-going pressure and anxiety.

The most effective treatment of IBS includes a programme of sensible dietary measures, combined with relaxation and stress-management techniques that address the mental and emotional problems. By choosing a treatment programme that goes beyond a purely physical approach and addresses the links between mind, emotions and physical experience, sufferers are likely to have the best chance of making a full recovery.

Recurrent Tension Headaches

If you suffer from frequent tension headaches, you should take a moment next time you feel under pressure to observe how you are holding the upper part of your body. There is a very good chance that you will discover that your shoulders feel tight, tense, and raised towards your ears. In addition your jaw is likely to be clenched in a vice-like grip, while the muscles of your arms are probably constricted and tight. The state of the latter can be most effectively assessed by observing how tightly you grab hold of a pen or a door handle. When you are tense, you tend to hold on far too tightly to small objects of this kind, with the result that the tautness is conveyed from your hands all the way up your arms to your shoulders and jaw.

Muscular tension of this kind restricts blood flow to the head, and can cause the muscles of the face and scalp to become tight and constricted. Generalized muscular tension that affects the neck and head in this way can have a direct effect in contributing to problems with tension headaches.

You may also unwittingly make the situation worse by reaching for the very items that may aggravate tension headaches. These may include coffee, alcohol, chocolate, sugary snacks and painkillers, which have been shown to trigger rebound headaches when used on a routine basis.

Effective ways of dealing with tension headaches include learning effective relaxation techniques, massage, avoiding food or drinks that trigger headaches, and exploring alternative medicines as effective, non-addictive sources of pain relief.

Psoriasis

Psoriasis is a most distressing skin condition that has a reputation for occurring on or being made much worse by exposure to stress. A familiar pattern often emerges where the raised, red, scaly areas so characteristic of psoriasis become much more severe after exposure to events that may be especially upsetting or stressful. Although psoriasis may be active during a period of strain, it is even more common for psoriasis sufferers to go through the traumatic time much as usual, thinking they have got away with it, only to find, to their dismay, that their condition gets worse as the stress eases. This is a commonly occurring situation with stress-related problems, rather similar to the migraine that emerges on holiday or at week-ends when the pressure of work is temporarily at bay.

Although skin conditions such as psoriasis and eczema are often considered to be of less dramatic importance, due to their non-life-threatening nature, it is very important to appreciate that conditions of this kind can have a significantly adverse effect on someone's quality of life. As a result of a general lack of understanding about skin conditions that look unhealthy (is it contagious? is it a surface expression of something more serious?), many patients who experience severe, widespread problems with psoriasis find that they suffer even more stress and anxiety as a result of the general lack of sensitivity and empathy shown by others.

Conventional treatment tends to rely on creams that can be applied on a regular basis to the patches of psoriasis. Unfortunately these tend to be unpleasant to use, due to their messy and smelly nature. In addition, light treatment may be used in severe or persistent situations, since controlled exposure to sunlight appears to improve symptoms temporarily in many cases. Nutritional therapy is worth exploring as a way of managing chronic skin problems, as well as alternative therapies such as homoeopathy, Western medical herbalism, and traditional Chinese medicine. The latter has a particularly impressive reputation in treating chronic skin problems successfully.

Illnesses That Can Cause Anxiety

Now it's time to consider the physical illnesses that can cause symptoms of anxiety. This is an important issue to consider, since by treating the physical imbalance that is setting off an anxiety state, very often there's an opportunity to improve the whole picture. In situations such as this, addressing only the symptoms of anxiety will lead to partial improvement at best. This is linked to the way in which the underlying problem must be dealt with before we can move on to truly improved mental, emotional and physical health.

Hyperthyroidism (Overactive Thyroid Gland)

An overactive thyroid gland can lead to a host of characteristically troublesome symptoms which may include any combination of the following: agitation, restlessness, weight loss, disturbed sleep pattern, palpitations, diarrhoea, hot flushes, breathlessness and generally feeling on edge. In developed cases, the eyes take on a characteristically large, bulging appearance. As with an underactive thyroid gland, diagnosis can be simply made by a blood test.

Diabetes

See the section on diabetes on page 38. Here you will find a general description of the variations within this general diagnostic term, and an explanation of diagnosis and treatment. Since mood swings can also be added to the list of possible symptoms that arise in connection with this condition, this is relevant to any discussion of anxiety-related problems.

ME (Myalgic Encephalitis)

Since ME can give rise to a number of symptoms that are likely to make someone feel powerless, weak and afraid, developing this condition can do a great deal to raise anxiety levels. More fuel may be added to anxiety levels if the sufferer is receiving medical treatment from a practitioner who still has doubts about the validity of ME as a diagnosable medical condition. For a general description of ME, its characteristic symptoms and possible avenues of the most appropriate treatment, see page 39.

Panic Attacks

If a panic attack descends for the first time and you have no idea what is happening to you, you are likely to be scared out of your skin. Some people may feel as though they are about to die, while others may be convinced that they are having a heart attack. This is because many of the common symptoms that occur during a panic attack mimic quite closely a number of features of a heart attack. These can include breathlessness, severe nausea and drenching sweats. However, what needs to be stressed, above all else, is that nowhere is there any evidence to suggest that anyone has come to serious harm or died as a result of a panic attack. This reassuring fact is something important to remember when you are in the throes of an acute episode of anxiety.

It is also extremely helpful to bear in mind that those who suffer from panic attacks on a regular or periodic basis have a range of practical measures open to them that can help them through the worst of an acute anxiety episode. This is especially relevant, since one of the most upsetting features of feeling the unmistakable early signs of panic is the disturbing sense of powerlessness that it can bring. Once this can be turned around with effective self-help measures that can support you through this upsetting experience, you are likely to find that attacks become shorter in duration and less severe in nature.

Panic attacks can begin in any number of situations, which may include any of the following:

● generally being under an excessive amount of stress that you feel powerless to manage or contain
● during the menopause, when panic attacks may accompany hot flushes or may occur on their own
● other times of major hormonal upheaval and change, such as following pregnancy or during puberty
● following a severe emotional shock or accident

One of the most dismaying features of panic attacks is that they can emerge for no obvious reason at all, making sufferers feel very vulnerable as a result. This is where self-help measures can play an important role. Practical, effective self-help measures to explore include learning relaxing, calm-inducing breathing techniques, relaxation techniques, and alternative medicines. In addition, nutritional advice and exploring appropriate exercise options can also form an important part of any anxiety-management plan. Practical advice on all of these areas may be found in Chapters Four to Eight of this book.

Characteristic Symptoms
Additional symptoms that are frequent features of panic attacks may include any of the following:

● dizziness or disorientation
● tingling in the extremities (the hands and the feet)
● muscle trembling

- palpitations (uncomfortable awareness of the heartbeat which may feel distressingly fast or irregular)
- an urgent need to empty the bowels
- feeling unable to breathe
- sensations of unreality or being distanced from familiar things

It may help to know that panic attacks are much more common than you might think, and that you are far from alone in suffering these unsettling symptoms. Estimates suggest that between 1 and 2 per cent of the population may experience panic attacks on a regular basis. A study conducted in the United States suggested that 35 per cent of the population (estimated at 87 million Americans) have experienced at least one panic attack. If we translate this percentage into a British context, this would imply that over 20 million people in this country may have experienced at least one episode of this distressing problem. It's just that most of us are unlikely to talk about these problems in the course of our day-to-day lives.

Attacks may last anything between 5 and 20 minutes, but your subjective experience may make a few minutes of panic feel like a lifetime. Some may be unfortunate and find that they go through waves of recurring episodes of panic where one runs into another. In such a situation sufferers may feel as though they are experiencing an episode that may last an hour or so.

Physical Reactions
The reason why people experience panic attacks appears to be linked to a process called the 'fight or flight' response. This is set in motion whenever the body is faced with a potential threat, with the physiological changes that occur preparing the body to take rapid action. These include blood sugar being released from the liver and sent to muscles that need extra energy, breathing becoming more rapid in order to maximize the amount of oxygen taken in, raised blood pressure, increased heart rate, reduced secretions such as saliva in the mouth (making the mouth feel dry), reduced digestive and bladder function, increased sweat, and muscle tension. All of these swift reactions are set in motion by adrenal gland activity, which secretes the stress hormones adrenaline and noradrenalin into the system.

Now, while these changes may be very appropriate and necessary when someone is confronted with a definite threat or pressure that requires decisive action, if these reactions are set in motion for no apparent reason you are likely to feel extremely uncomfortable and disturbed. When this happens you experience the dry mouth, nausea, muscle trembling, shortness of breath and palpitations that are part and parcel of a panic attack.

Common Phobias

These involve symptoms that are parallel to those experienced in a panic attack, but tend to be set off in anticipation of, or in direct response to, being exposed to a specific situation. This could include any of the following: from being in open spaces, speaking in public, being confronted with a spider, birds, mice, vomiting, illness, being alone, heights, or flying. The potential range of phobic situations is very wide indeed, with most triggers being irrational in nature. For example, there is absolutely no point in trying to explain to someone with a fear of spiders that the average British domestic spider is not going to harm them, and that it is much smaller than the person who is afraid of it. However, those who experience panic attacks may begin to develop specific aversions and phobias of places or situations that they come to associate with the onset of an acute anxiety episode.

Some people find that they can cope with their daily lives quite easily because their phobias don't tend to impinge on their everyday activities. On the other hand, if the phobia that they suffer from limits their activities in a severe way (such as an agoraphobic finding that they are unable to leave the house without a great deal of support), they should seek professional advice. This should be done in order to help sufferers come to terms with the source of their problems. This help could take the form of psychotherapy or counselling. In addition, an alternative form of medical support such as homoeopathy could do a great deal to relieve symptoms of panic and anxiety.

Post-Traumatic Stress Syndrome

This condition is likely to emerge in response to experiencing a severely disturbing and traumatic experience. Often problems emerge after the event, with symptoms including poor sleep pattern, unpredictable recurrence of flashbacks, a sense of unreality, panic attacks, and hyperventilation. Professional support is essential, with help being provided from counselling and psychological therapists. Extra help may also be gained from appropriate alternative medical therapies and positive changes in lifestyle.

Chapter Two

Understanding Depression

There many ways of referring to feeling depressed which cover the wide spectrum of this negative state of mind. Some might say they are 'feeling blue' or 'down in the dumps' if they are having an off day or two, within the overall framework of what is normally a fairly balanced emotional experience. The chances are that there will have been a trigger that set this state of mind off, and that once people have a chance to make the necessary emotional and mental adjustments, they will be back on course once again.

Others might say that they are 'feeling flat' or 'lacking in sparkle'. If this happens on a regular or cyclical basis, sufferers may find that it is not enough to wait until the mood passes, since they may feel uneasy about its descending again within the near future. This is the sort of situation where self-help is a good place to start, so that positive ways can be found to enhance mental and emotional equilibrium in whatever ways might seem appropriate. This may include anything from making sure that you get enough rest and relaxation to improving your daily diet or taking up regular exercise. If these changes yield positive results, this is likely to give you the necessary confidence, resolve and commitment to stick to these lifestyle improvements.

There is, however, an experience of depression beyond this point where you may feel in such a black and destructive state of mind that everything appears negative and hopeless. In this state of severe depression, the bottom may seem to have dropped out of life, leaving you feeling acutely lonely, despairing, vulnerable and fearful of what life holds in store. When depression of this kind descends, you need access to as much support as possible from professional, medical and complementary sources. Once effective treatment has begun, you may well be in a position to explore self-help strategies as an extra source of essential help.

Some people may not need any external triggers for a bout of depression to descend, since they may have a temperament or family history that predisposes them to depressive illness. However, some upheavals and changes that are part and parcel of life can be responsible for leaving you more vulnerable to developing depression.

During pregnancy or following childbirth
Depressive feelings may be triggered off as a result of the profound hormonal shifts that occur during pregnancy. These changes in hormonal secretions can lead some women to feel a sense of elation, while others may feel quite the opposite. The same is true following childbirth, when some mothers feel a surge of profound love and positive emotion that bonds them to their newborn baby, while others may feel flat, angry, resentful or distant. Depression may also set in as a result of the sheer exhaustion involved in trying to meet the constantly demanding needs of a young baby, especially if the experience of labour was arduous, problematic, or just downright disappointing. This can be made even more difficult and complicated if other family members are feeling left out and neglected once a newborn is the centre of attention.

Bereavement
Experiencing the loss of someone very close can expose you to a range of emotions that may take you by surprise, both in their overwhelming intensity and their nature. Some people may initially feel a sense of shock and numbness, followed by a profound feeling of grief, loss, and an acute sense of emotional pain that the person who was loved can never be seen again. Some may experience an overwhelming sense of anger that takes them by surprise. This anger and aggression may be directed at the dead person who has abandoned them, or at members of the medical profession who have seemingly let them down. Guilt and regret can also arise during the process of grieving, especially if you feel that you did not take or were denied the opportunity to say all that you needed to before the end.

However, it is also very important to recognize that it is perfectly natural to feel a profound sense of relief at the death of a person you may have loved very much. Although it may sound extremely harsh or contradictory, it may be perfectly appropriate to feel a natural sense of relief at the release of someone who may have been visibly suffering or painfully fearful in their final illness.

If you are able to experience, acknowledge, and release these emotions as they naturally arise, the chances are that you will be able to grieve as you must if you are to deepen your emotional experience and move on with your life. Unfortunately, if these emotions are repressed or denied for any reason, you may find that you begin to experience symptoms of depression rather than grief. This may especially be the case if you bottle up feelings of anger, guilt or resentment, which you may unwittingly turn against yourself.

Redundancy and Unexpected Changes in Lifestyle

Jobs provide us with far more than financial security. Many people derive a profound sense of satisfaction from their careers, and as a consequence may also feel that their personal identity is very much bound up with the job that they do.

While it may be unhealthy and unbalanced for anyone unduly and exclusively to identify with their professional identity, many find that doing a job well provides them with a strong sense of satisfaction. It is also true that the more demanding and stressful a job is, the greater the sense of satisfaction we are likely to derive from it.

As a result, being made unexpectedly redundant may have a profound effect, making you lose a great deal of self-esteem as well as directly threatening your sense of identity and making you feel you have failed. This is likely to have an even more serious impact if you experience the loss of a job in your fifties, since this is a time when you may have already been experiencing the disturbing and unsettling emotions of a mid-life crisis.

If you are made redundant in the midst of other unresolved issues regarding the meaning and significance of your life, the scene may be set for depression to follow. On the other hand, if you approach redundancy or any other major shift in your fortunes from a more balanced emotional perspective, the situation is still going to be difficult and painful, but you may be surprised at the unexpected opportunities that present themselves once you have gone through this major upheaval in your life.

Some people may embrace the possibility of 'downshifting' with gusto, realizing that they may have been unwitting prisoners to a high mortgage and a pressured lifestyle which left precious little room for relaxation and quality time. Others may find that as a relationship breaks up they have the chance of moving on to a different phase of life where their sense of individuality can flourish, perhaps for the first time.

Ageing

Although we all know that ageing is an inevitable fact, the way in which people respond to the changes that occur in their emotions, minds and bodies as the years pass by will have a great deal to do with their individual make-up. Some may reach a state of acceptance where they adapt and change with the signs of ageing as they appear. Others may refuse to 'give in' and may find ways of disguising the ageing process, and live life with as much energy and vitality as they can muster.

How you approach the reality of growing older will have a great deal to do with the way in which your parents responded to the process of ageing, your life experience, and your general state of health. Above all, your capacity to be flexible and your ability to adapt will have a great bearing on how you cope with getting older. Those who have trouble admitting to feeling vulnerable, fearful and distressed may have greater problems with ageing. If you are unable to share your worries and rely instead on keeping a 'stiff upper lip', there is a danger that you may become depressed and fearful as you get older. Bracing yourself constantly against the inevitable, and trying to maintain control at all costs, is an emotionally costly business. All it tends to lead to is exhaustion and tension. On the other hand, learning how to move 'with the flow' can open up possibilities for acceptance which can be surprisingly liberating.

The Menopause

Although it is by no means inevitable, some women discover that they experience symptoms of depression as they move through menopause. While this may be partly due to dramatic shifts in hormone levels (with oestrogen and progesterone secretion dropping sharply), it also appears to be related to how each woman approaches the concept of ageing, as well as to her response to domestic factors such as coping with children becoming independent and leaving home. The latter can be interpreted as a form of liberation or loss, depending on how women feel at this time. Physical changes such as the appearance of wrinkles, greying hair and weight gain can come as a shock and take some time to adjust to. In addition, common menopausal symptoms such as sleep disturbance, hot flushes, night sweats and changes in libido provide some challenges that women may find difficult to deal with.

On the other hand, it is important to stress that this transitional phase of life need not be automatically traumatic or depressing, provided women are well prepared for what realistically to expect, and well versed in strategies that will help them make the transition as smoothly as possible. The best route for exploring these issues may be found in the many self-help books on the market which provide the facts of menopause, while also offering essential information on the conventional and alternative medical support available.

Reactive and Non-Reactive Depression

Depression is sometimes divided into two different types of the illness, referred to as *reactive* and *endogenous* (non-reactive) depression. Reactive depression has been used to refer to depressive symptoms that descend after exposure to an external trigger, while endogenous depression has been used to refer to depression that arises from 'within' (in other words, without any external negative stress or trigger to set it off).

The situation and terminology has now changed somewhat, with 'reactive' and 'endogenous' being used to describe a broad spectrum of depression. As a result, reactive depression is regarded as a milder expression of the problem, while endogenous depression is considered more severe.

Characteristic Symptoms

The following are the most common and characteristic features of depression. However, as shall be seen in the case histories that follow, different symptoms arise, with different rates of intensity in each person. Some common symptoms may not appear at all, while other, less expected features may be especially marked. This is something that alternative therapists are especially aware of, since most therapies with a holistic perspective work from the basis that they treat people, not just disease symptoms. As a result, tremendous emphasis is put on finding what makes each individual unique.

Having said this, there are common symptoms that those who suffer depression tend to share, which include:

- poor quality, disturbed sleep with a tendency to wake early (often around 4 to 5 a.m.)
- marked sense of distress on waking, which may take the form of anxious or depressed thought patterns
- digestive problems which may include indigestion, churning in the stomach on waking, loss of appetite, nausea, heartburn, and possible alternation between diarrhoea and constipation
- weight loss through lack of interest in food, or weight gain through comfort eating
- lack of interest and excitement in aspects of life that would previously have been compelling or absorbing
- recurring and persistent negative thought patterns (these may include thoughts of self-harm or harm to loved ones)
- palpitations (awareness of rapid or irregular heartbeat) and/or hyperventilation (breathing rapidly and shallowly from the upper chest)
- poor levels of concentration and poor memory
- abrupt or severe changes of mood, which may include overwhelming feelings of indifference, apathy, sadness, hopelessness, anxiety, despondency or despair
- lowered or absent libido
- extreme fatigue and lack of mental, emotional and physical energy
- suppressed or unacknowledged depressive feelings may be linked to the emergence or aggravation of physical conditions such as rheumatoid arthritis or asthma

Jim's Story
Jim was a very high-powered, energetic senior executive. Becoming self-employed proved to be more stressful than anticipated, and he began to develop stress-related symptoms such as interrupted sleep pattern, lowered energy levels and digestive problems. He tried to

ignore these as much as possible, but things did not improve, and he eventually collapsed at work with severe tightness in the chest, hyperventilation and chest pains. He was rushed to hospital, where all the relevant tests were done; he was found to be free of any obvious physical problems.

This episode left Jim feeling vulnerable, frightened and out of control for the first time in his life. To make matters worse, he began to feel that he no longer had control over his thoughts, with negative ideas coming into his mind at random. It also disturbed him greatly that these thoughts could be sparked off by other people's conversation, or a television or newspaper feature. His sleep pattern was getting increasingly disturbed, with some nights going by where he would be waking each hour.

Jim felt strongly about not wanting to take conventional antidepressants or tranquillizers unless they were absolutely necessary, and wanted to find an alternative route of support. His doctor was very supportive of Jim's wishes and suggested that he might benefit from seeing a clinical psychologist. This was the state of play when Jim arrived in my consulting room.

With a combination of a regular exercise regime, homoeopathic treatment and talking through his feelings about his crisis, so that he realized he was not alone in suffering these symptoms, Jim made steady progress. He responded well to the homoeopathic remedy Nux vomica, which gradually restored him to his previously healthy sleep pattern. As a result of refreshing sleep and appropriate, regular exercise, his normally high energy levels re-emerged, and his negative thought patterns steadily receded to the background. Jim is now productively back at work, but recognizes when he is doing too much, and makes releasing the pressure his top priority.

Trisha's Story
When Trisha first came to see me she was seeking help for her rheumatoid arthritis symptoms, which had emerged suddenly six months before. After taking a detailed history of her physical symptoms, I went on to ask about her emotional health. It transpired that her father had died suddenly just a few weeks before the emergence of her arthritic symptoms. When we explored this issue further it became clear that Trisha had felt unable to access her feelings of grief at her father's death, mainly because their relationship had

been fraught with difficulty and lack of communication. Over a number of appointments it became noticeable that Trisha had felt an overwhelming sense of anger towards her father during his lifetime, which had been suppressed from the time of his death.

During her months of treatment I suggested Trisha should eliminate items of food from her diet which are known to make inflammation of the joints worse (red meat, white sugar, tomatoes and citrus fruit). In addition the homoeopathic remedy Staphisagria was prescribed for her, one of the most commonly prescribed remedies for problems that arise from anger that is suppressed and turned inwards. The turning point in her treatment came when Trisha told me that she had had a dream about her father where she was able to express her emotions more forcefully than she had ever been able to do in her waking hours. For a few days her rheumatoid arthritis symptoms flared up, followed by a steady improvement.

Julie's Story
Julie's life was going well until she became pregnant. Her baby was planned and very much wanted, but Julie found, to her dismay, that once she was three months into her pregnancy she became extremely tearful, and felt on an emotional roller coaster. This continued throughout her pregnancy, and to Julie's distress did not change after her son was born.

Concerned about feeling unable to look after herself, her son, or her partner, Julie sought psychiatric help and was put on a course of antidepressants. This seemed to help temporarily in stabilizing her mood, but unfortunately Julie's mood swings returned despite using the medication. Various formulations of antidepressants were tried, but with little lasting success.

By the time Julie came for homoeopathic help she felt at the end of the line. Her energy levels had plummeted to zero, making her stay in bed at times. Going out would feel impossible on a bad day, since at those times all that Julie could cope with was being alone.

Crying provided no release, just leaving her more mentally, emotionally and physically tired.

Although she felt she wanted to sleep all of the time since being depressed (sometimes up to 10 hours a night), waking every morning was an effort, because sleep wasn't providing any sense of rest or relaxation. Julie felt an overwhelming sense of despair at her isolation and having lost control of her life.

After just one month of homoeopathic treatment with the homoeopathic remedy Pulsatilla (which has a profound effect in helping re-balance the whole system following a time of hormonal upheaval), Julie reported an extraordinary improvement.

After the first ten days of treatment she had felt free of bouts of weepiness, apathy and flatness. Energy levels were fine and she had broken free of her negative perspective on going out and socializing. Sleep quality was also restored, and for the first time in ages Julie felt she could get enough rest from six hours of good-quality sleep a night.

Related Physical Problems

Many people may assume that when they are depressed, this is a disorder that is primarily associated with the mind. While this is partly true, we also have to take on board the way in which our mental, emotional and physical sense of well-being is interlinked. As a result, any imbalance which profoundly affects one level of health and well-being tends to have a knock-on effect elsewhere.

The field of study called psycho-neuro-immunology has done a great deal to draw attention to the way in which one's mental state and emotional health can have a profound effect on physical health. Studies conducted at Mount Sinai Hospital in New York have demonstrated how protracted grieving and depression can have a direct effect in raising the risk of developing hardening of the arteries, high blood pressure and on-going digestive problems. On the other hand, deliberately recalling positive, pleasant, pleasurable experiences can do the reverse, by stimulating enhanced immune system functioning and making us feel more relaxed.

There are certain physical problems that can emerge alongside depression.

Lack of Appetite
One of the most noticeable things about feeling depressed is the way that you lose interest and pleasure in the things that normally make up the fabric of life. As a result, it is very common for a depressed person to find that they no longer have the spark of interest in the sensual pleasures that they would normally experience. This may

include lack of delight in eating, listening to music, conversation, or sex. In many cases, pleasure in all of these areas may seem to depart.

Eating can also pose particular problems when someone feels depressed, since, as with Julie's case above, the natural tendency when people feel low is to retreat into themselves and avoid contact with other people. Sometimes this is done because they find other people irritating or demanding, or sometimes because they feel guilty about burdening others with their company. Since mealtimes are fundamentally sociable in their nature, this can have an adverse effect on how people feel about eating. However, the good news is that as symptoms recede into the background, capacity for pleasure also returns in equal measure.

Indigestion
Social issues aside, there are also practical problems that can be associated with feeling depressed that put us off eating. Some people find that if they feel a combination of stress, anxiety and depression, they can experience acute digestive discomfort that puts them off their food. Common sensations include acidity and churning of the stomach, with a sense of food taking a very long time to be broken down and digested. This situation is made even worse if they eat large meals late at night, since this can lead to severe problems with heartburn once they are lying down.

There is the additional complication that you may be drawn to the most unsuitable foods when you feel depressed, since these foods are quick and easy to prepare (sometimes needing no preparation at all) at a time when you feel you just can't be bothered with anything more complicated. Offending items would include junk foods of any shape or form, 'instant' meals that just involve adding water, chips, crisps, full-fat cheeses, or heavy puddings (which tend to include a hefty proportion of fat and white sugar).

Bingeing and Comfort Eating
While all that has been said above is true, some people may respond to feeling depressed by going in the opposite direction and searching for temporary solace and comfort in food. Eating patterns of this kind are not linked to hunger, but more to a need for a sense of physical comfort. As a result, food cravings are likely to centre on items that are either very starchy, fatty and stodgy in nature (crisps, chips,

pastries and puddings) or sweet (chocolate, cakes and sweet, fizzy drinks).

Sadly, once you are into comfort eating in this way it is likely to have a destructive effect when you are feeling depressed, since it is probably going to leave you with a weight problem as well. Since self-esteem is almost always at a low ebb when we are depressed, bingeing can make matters even worse. However, once your depressed perspective eases in response to appropriate treatment, there is a very good chance that you will be able to make the necessary positive changes in your eating patterns in order to improve your health.

Extreme Fatigue

Although this distressing and debilitating symptom can arise for a host of other reasons, depression almost always has a marked impact in causing energy levels to plummet. If you are depressed and complain of feeling as though you are wading through treacle when you attempt to get the smallest task done, it is always a good idea for thyroid function, blood sugar levels and iron levels to be checked, since physical problems of this kind can make severe fatigue much worse. However, if these are assessed and you still feel mentally, emotionally and physically exhausted, it is most likely to be caused by feeling depressed.

This pervading sense of fatigue can be partly due to the disturbed sleep pattern that is part and parcel of depression, since unsatisfactory sleep quality deprives you of an essential way of recharging your mental, emotional and physical energy levels. Too much sleep of poor quality is not the answer to this problem, unfortunately, since it is the depth of sleep that determines whether we wake feeling refreshed or not.

In addition, depression has the direct effect of draining you of the stimulation or 'energizing influences' which you can respond to on a daily basis when you are feeling in mental and emotional harmony. These energizing influences can include listening to a favourite piece of music, enjoying a film, feeling the satisfaction of a job well done, engaging in playful banter with colleagues, experiencing an unexpected kindness from a stranger, being on the receiving end of a smile, or making love. However, if you are feeling negative and flat you are unlikely to be able to respond positively to any of these influences, or even worse, may interpret them as insincere or manipulative gestures.

Extra problems can also arise when you are feeling very low, since you are unlikely to feel capable of eating in a way that maximizes levels of energy and vitality, or of your engaging in energy-boosting exercise. This is something that tends to become possible once you begin to make some positive steps towards recovery.

Illnesses that Can Cause Depression

Now we have looked at the physical problems that can arise as a result of depression, it's time to consider the physical illnesses that can trigger symptoms of depression. This is an important issue to consider, since when the physical imbalance that is leading to the depressive symptoms is treated, very often the whole picture improves. In such situations addressing just the symptoms of depression will at best yield partial results, since the underlying problem must be addressed before we can move on to experience truly improved mental, emotional and physical health.

Hypothyroidism (Underactive Thyroid)
The characteristic symptoms that arise as a result of an underactive thyroid gland can very often be confused with a state of clinical depression, since they include severe fatigue, digestive disturbance (often including slowed-down digestive function and severe constipation), flatness of mood and weight gain. However, there are additional symptoms which are not characteristic features of depression and which can help form an initial differentiating diagnosis. These may include any combination of the following: dry skin and hair, loss or thinning of hair, hoarseness and deepening of tone of the voice, and a severe sense of chilliness. For a firm confirmation of a diagnosis of this easily treatable condition, all that is required is a simple blood test.

Diabetes
Adult-onset diabetes (often referred to as Type 2 diabetes) is a treatable condition that can often be regulated in adults by dietary control. This involves strictly regulating one's intake of sugar, and keeping blood sugar levels stable by eating small amounts every couple of hours. If this is not proving enough to keep the condition within

stable boundaries, then a form of insulin may be taken by mouth in order to give additional support. Blood sugar levels can be easily monitored at home by using a small machine, which analyses a drop of blood to reveal the current blood sugar reading, or by strips that can be dipped into a fresh urine sample. Symptoms which overlap with depression include mental and physical lack of energy, weakness, apathy and weight loss. Differentiating symptoms include marked thirst, increased urine output, and constantly dry mouth.

Anaemia
A reduced number of red blood cells can cause you to feel exhausted, lightheaded and low. If you become anaemic, it can usually be speedily rectified by supplementing with extra iron, but a close eye should be kept on the situation, since in some cases a low red blood cell count can be indicative of other underlying problems. If anaemia is suspected, ask your doctor if he or she thinks a blood test is in order.

ME (Myalgic Encephalitis)
This has been an extremely controversial medical subject, since the medical profession has been divided in the past about the very existence of this condition. However, opinion has been slowly changing, with an emerging consensus of professional opinion acknowledging that this condition is not merely 'all in the mind'. Many symptoms of this debilitating illness can overlap noticeably with features of depression, and may include any of the following: poor sleep pattern and sleep quality, headaches, digestive discomfort and bloating, cramping pains with diarrhoea, muscle weakness, persistent mental exhaustion, mood swings (which may include bouts of weepiness), depression, panic, irritability or severe anxiety.

Unfortunately there is as yet no conclusive test that can confirm a diagnosis of ME, but there are certain factors that appear to leave people vulnerable to developing this controversial condition. These include a chronically stressful lifestyle that leaves no space for relaxation and de-stressing, a dependence on stimulants and relaxants in order to keep up the pace (these may include anything from coffee, alcohol and cigarettes to recreational or prescription drugs), reliance on 'quick fix' or junk foods, a history of recurrent minor infections that may have been treated with routine courses of antibiotics, or contracting a severe viral illness that you have not been able to recover fully from. As a result, the latter may leave you feeling permanently under par, or you may experience recurrent bouts of a similar problem at regular intervals.

The most effective treatment for ME (or Chronic Fatigue Syndrome, as it is sometimes called) tends to be a combination of alternative, complementary and conventional therapies. Good possibilities to consider include Western medical herbalism, traditional Chinese medicine, homoeopathy and nutritional therapy.

Seasonal Affective Disorder (SAD)

Most people are likely to have experienced a sinking feeling as they look outside and see a vista of grey skies, when the world appears to be colourless and uninspiring. However, if their emotional life is in a state of general balance, the chances are that they are soon distracted by something else and forget about the bleak, uninspiring scene outside.

Those who suffer from recurrent depression in the autumn and winter months are faced with a more intense situation which requires attention in order to give them the maximum chance of recovery. The symbolism of the seasons can have a particular resonance when we are depressed, with autumn and winter visibly bringing home the reality of ageing and death. On the other hand, for those who do not suffer from depression, this knowledge tends to be balanced out by the promise of re-birth and renewal in spring and summer.

If you know that your negative moods intensify greatly in the winter months, you might consider how you can increase your exposure to bright sunlight. If a winter holiday break is not practically possible, you might consider investing in installing some full-spectrum lighting, which appears to help those who suffer from seasonal affective disorder by increasing their exposure to bright light. This can be especially helpful during the shortened days of November to February.

ChapterThree

Conventional Medical Help

What to Expect from Your Doctor

Increasingly, large numbers of patients are consulting their family doctors with generally stress-related problems. A high proportion of these will be suffering from the symptoms of anxiety and/or depression.

For some people, receiving an initial diagnosis of depression may be a generally positive experience since they may have been convinced that they had a more serious, life-threatening condition. Some may also feel relieved when they feel that something practical is being done to help them, in the form of drug treatment or counselling. For many, just being able to put their feelings, fears and symptoms into words may feel immensely helpful, since this may be the first opportunity they have had to talk about their problems since they began feeling ill.

During the consultation your doctor will want to gain as clear a picture as possible of the symptoms that are troubling you. In addition, questions will be asked about stress levels at the moment, if there has been a bereavement or break-up of a relationship, how things are going at work, and what your quality of life is like at home. It may be that there are obvious triggers that have set off problems with anxiety and depression, and your doctor may feel confident enough to make an initial diagnosis on the spot, suggesting a course of medication and making sure that a return appointment is made within a short interval of time. This may also be the case if you have previously suffered from these conditions and your doctor is fairly confident that this a recurrence of the same problem.

If there is any doubt about the diagnosis, your doctor will want to rule out the possibility of any other medical condition that could give rise to similar symptoms. In order to do this he or she is likely to conduct a physical examination, and will probably want to send some blood for analysis. If these tests don't suggest that there is an underlying physical cause for the symptoms, your doctor is likely to conclude his original tentative diagnosis of anxiety and depression is correct.

Once a diagnosis has been made, what follows may be guided by a combination of your doctor's experienced opinion and your own personal preferences with regard to treatment. If you feel strongly that you do not want to go for the support of drug treatment initially, your doctor may be happy to recommend a psychological route of treatment. The drawback of this approach, however, is that there can be a very long waiting list for this sort of treatment on the NHS (anything from six months up to a year). If you have private medical insurance this can speed things up, but unfortunately not all policies cover psychiatric problems.

If you have very strong opinions about wanting to avoid going down the route of conventional drug treatment, and you are suffering from mild to moderate symptoms, some doctors may be happy for you to try an alternative kind of medical treatment, such as using St John's Wort under supervision while you are waiting for extra support to emerge from a counsellor or psychologist.

However, it is important to stress that a great deal depends on the severity of the symptoms you are experiencing. If these are especially problematic and disruptive, it may be that your doctor advises that extra treatment from a conventional antidepressant is a 'must' in order to prevent the problem from escalating.

If this is the case, it can be helpful to bear in mind that the appropriate and responsible use of conventional antidepressants can be a life-saver in cases where severe depression and anxiety have descended in response to a trigger of obvious trauma. In such situations, these medicines can give you the 'buffer' you may need in order to give you the space within which to get your life back in order. Once they have done their job and you have moved on, you may well feel that you are ready to begin a supervised withdrawal of medication with the guidance of a sympathetic doctor or psychiatrist.

Always remember that what needs to be worked out is the 'risk/ benefit ratio' of taking conventional drugs. If you believe that the potential risks of side-effects outweigh the distress you are feeling, you would be better placed to explore other ways of supporting yourself to recovery. On the other hand, if the very fabric of your life (your intimate relationships, career and financial security) is being threatened by the severity of your symptoms (especially if there are any indications that you are approaching a suicidal state of mind), the severity of the threat to the quality of your life may obviously outweigh the drawbacks of the potential side-effects of taking conventional medication.

Conventional Medical Support

What follows is not an exhaustive list of all of the different possible drugs that may be chosen from by the average doctor, but it does aim to give a broad idea of the main categories of drugs which an average doctor is likely to consider when selecting a treatment regime for a patient suffering from anxiety and depression.

Drugs Used to Treat Anxiety

Until relatively recently, tranquillizers were regarded as the 'drug of choice' for those who suffered from anxiety. Unfortunately, the severe problems of side-effects and dependency caused by these drugs which belong to the benzodiazepine group have meant they are no longer considered the appropriate treatment for anxiety. These drugs are especially unacceptable for treating nervous or anxious patients, since they can exaggerate symptoms of anxiety and sleeplessness when taken over an extended period of time. Patients have also found themselves dependent on tranquillizers needing escalating doses in order to maintain any calming effect. Once dependent on this form of medication, patients attempting to cut down their medication have found that the withdrawal symptoms have been unacceptably severe. It has been estimated by some patients that withdrawal from benzodiazepines is more traumatic than coming off heroin or cocaine.

As a result of the hazards of benzodiazepine use, doctors should not prescribe them for a period exceeding two weeks. It has been established since the 1980s that taking these drugs for more than a month, even in doses considered to be therapeutic, may lead to dependence. In many cases of anxiety, doctors are more likely to prescribe an antidepressant that has sedative properties in favour of a tranquillizer. However, although prescription rates of tranquillizers in the UK have been cut from 31 million in the late 1970s to approximately 18 million per year, those who are already addicted face a difficult battle in returning to a normal life.

As can be seen, tranquillizers are best avoided where possible, and if they are prescribed it should never be for a period in excess of four weeks. The same is also true of the more recently introduced hypnotic drugs, since they appear to carry similar risks to benzodiazepines.

Sometimes a doctor may suggest the use of drugs called beta-blockers in order to suppress the symptoms of acute anxiety. Although beta-blockers are mainly intended to treat patients who suffer from high blood pressure, they may sometimes be used in the short-term management of the physical manifestations of anxiety symptoms. However, caution needs to be used, since in common with all conventional drugs, beta-blockers have side-effects. These may include aggravation of breathing difficulties in asthmatics, symptoms of circulatory sluggishness (such as unusually cold hands and feet), and a subjective, general sense of the whole system being slowed down.

Drugs Used to Treat Depression

Modern antidepressants fall into one of three main groups of drugs: the SSRIs (selective serotonin re-uptake inhibitors), MAOIs (monoamine oxidase inhibitors), and Tricyclics. Antidepressants are thought to work by acting on the neurotransmitters noradrenolin, epinephrine and serotonin, restoring them to optimum levels in the depressed patient. Selecting an appropriate antidepressant for a patient can involve a great deal of experience, patience and creative prescribing on the part of a physician. It is worth bearing in mind that someone should not give up if the first course of antidepressant therapy has been unable to stimulate an improvement. This can be due to a number of factors, that may include any of the following:

● Lack of persistence: It has been estimated that antidepressants can take up to six weeks before the beneficial effects become apparent. Because of the fairly lengthy time-scale involved, it is very important to give a course of treatment enough time before assessing how helpful it is.

- Incorrect prescription for meeting the individual needs of the patient: Because there is such a choice of different formulas of antidepressant available, it is very important to bear in mind that lack of response to one approach doesn't mean that another may not be suitable. Unfortunately, this form of trial and error can take a little while to resolve itself, and does require a great deal of patience on the part of doctors and patients. This is especially true for the latter, since they are the ones who are suffering the symptoms.
- Training of the prescriber: Doctors may be very well equipped to diagnose and treat straightforward cases of depression. However, there are some situations where the expertise of the doctor is too general, and the more specialized skills of a psychiatrist are needed. This is an option well worth considering if improvement is slow and a number of antidepressants have been tried by your doctor, with little or no success. Psychiatrists have the advantage of being more knowledgeable about different variations of antidepressants, scales of dosage, and possible side-effects. As a result, they may well feel more open to the possibilities of prescribing less popular drugs, or giving dosages that fall outside the standard range.
- Severity of symptoms: As a general rule, the more intense the symptoms are, the longer it may take to see sustained improvement. In common with oher drugs, antidepressants have an effect sometimes referred to as a 'half-life', which can be understood as the build-up of the drug in the system of the patient. Once this 'cruising level' of the antidepressant has been reached, signs of improvement often become obvious. Since very severe cases of depression may need to be treated with higher doses of antidepressant drugs than the average recommended therapeutic dose for treating mild to moderate depression, it can take longer for this 'cruising level' to be reached in the system.
- If there are any indications that suggest that symptoms are becoming progressively severe in response to antidepressant treatment, or that troublesome or disturbing side-effects are emerging, this must be communicated to your practitioner. This sort of reaction would suggest that a different antidepressant formula may be more suitable for you.

SSRIs

These are generally regarded as a huge breakthrough in the development of antidepressant formulas, since they appear to avoid some of the pitfalls of the older MAOIs and tricyclic medications. SSRIs include the controversial antidepressant Prozac, as well as lesser-known names such as Cipramil and Seroxat. Potential side-effects may include digestive upsets such as nausea and diarrhoea, disturbed sleep pattern, and possible increase in jitteriness and anxiety. It has been suggested that these side-effects should be temporary in nature, and should clear up within approximately two to three weeks of use.

Unlike tranquillizers, which have been shown to bring problems of addiction in their wake, SSRIs do not appear to lead to the same problems. However, there are some reservations about their use that need to be borne in mind if you want to make an informed decision. These include lack of knowledge about what the effects of long-term use of SSRIs might be, since these are relative newcomers in the treatment of depression. The effects of taking SSRIs when pregnant are also unclear. Bearing in mind that these drugs have only been in use for approximately twelve years, it can take a much more extended period of time for long-term effects to emerge. Some patients may also be unhappy with the exaggerated symptoms of insomnia, anxiety and agitation that arise at the initial period of use of SSRIs. There is an additional possibility of extremely vivid dreams or nightmares occurring in response to this form of medication. Unfortunately, SSRIs also can have a negative effect on sexual performance and libido, SSRIs may have the distressing tendency to render the patient unable to reach orgasm. A recent study revealed that one-third of patients who participated in the study reported a generally decreased interest in sex. Care also needs to be taken not to combine an SSRI antidepressant with any other form of medication which can raise serotonin levels. Always consult your doctor or pharmacist if you are unsure about any alternative medication you may be taking.

Always bear in mind that, although this category of antidepressant may be considered more refined than the older formulas described below, what matters most is your own, individual response to an antidepressant. Some people may indeed find that a drug such as Prozac suits them down to the ground, while others may find that it just doesn't agree with them. Always feel free to express any reservations that you may have about your reactions to your physician, rather than feeling uneasy about putting up with reactions which are becoming genuinely disturbing or uncomfortable.

Tricyclics
The drugs that fall into this group include the thoroughly road-tested Prothiaden. Developed in the 1950s, these drugs were considered for three decades or so to be much safer than the antidepressants that fall into the MAOI category (these are described below). However, as with any drug, it emerged that there were various drawbacks in the form of side-effects. These include persistently dry mouth, visual disturbance, weight gain, loss of libido, muscle twitching, low energy levels, and possible irregular heartbeat. Care must also be taken not to combine tricyclic medication with other drugs such as anti-histamines. These drugs are also thought to have adverse effects when consumed with alcohol and/or cigarettes.

However, although there are undoubted drawbacks to these antidepressants, they should not be dismissed automatically in favour of newer drugs. It is simply the case that some individuals may tolerate a tricyclic better than an SSRI. This may be especially true of patients who respond well to the overall effects of this type of antidepressant.

MAOIs
These were the very earliest form of antidepressant available. They are seldom used these days, since the newer forms of medication described above are regarded as much safer, and as a result more attractive to patient and prescriber alike.

The main problem associated with MAOIs is their tendency to cause side-effects, and the serious interaction that can occur if they are combined with fairly innocuous food items. Possible side-effects include raised blood pressure, and adverse effects if MAOIs are combined with alternative forms of antidepressants.

The restrictions imposed on users of these antidepressants are also considerable, since any of the following foods can have an adverse effect when combined with taking an MAOI: cheese; yoghurt; fermented foods such as wine, breads, pickles and anything else containing yeast; items that have monosodium glutamate added;

smoked, processed meats; soya products; and figs. As you can see, in contrast with more recent developments in antidepressant medication, MAOIs present the patient with a range of restrictions that can make life limiting and complicated.

Lithium

Although this drug tends to be reserved for treating cases of manic depression (a condition which involves alternating episodes of euphoria and depression), there are specific situations where it may be used in the treatment of especially severe cases of depression, where the expected improvement has not occurred in response to antidepressant medication. In these situations, lithium may be prescribed side-by-side with an antidepressant such as a Tricyclic or SSRI. However, it is important to bear in mind that lithium is a potentially very toxic drug which can cause serious problems if it is allowed to reach toxic doses in the system. As a result, once lithium is being used on a regular basis, blood tests must be done every three months in order to check kidney function. Initially, blood tests are likely to be carried out on a weekly basis until the lithium level has stabilized. In addition, those who take lithium must be careful about adverse interaction with other conventional drugs such as diuretics.

Possible side-effects include weight gain, initial loss of appetite, headache, an unpleasant taste in the mouth and loose stools. If any of the following symptoms arise in anyone who is taking lithium, they should arrange to have a blood test immediately: severe thirst, excessive urination, vomiting, diarrhoea, marked trembling of the hands, slurred speech and poor co-ordination.

Using Self-help Strategies Alongside Conventional Medicines

There are a great many positive options for additional self-help if you are taking conventional medication for anxiety and/or depression. None of these extra methods of support should offer any risk of conflict in therapeutic terms, but should give you a greater sense of confidence and empowerment in helping speed your recovery.

As the following sections on the use of complementary and alternative therapies suggest, you need not have any worries about toxic, chemical interaction if you choose to use homoeopathic medicines side by side with conventional medication. This is due to the highly diluted nature of homoeopathic remedies, which renders them especially safe. They produce no adverse reactions when taken alongside conventional drugs. The very worst scenario may be that in some cases conventional medication may hamper or interfere with the full therapeutic value of homoeopathic remedies selected on a self-help basis. This is by no means the rule or inevitable, so it is well worth introducing extra homoeopathic support at various stages of treatment. This can be especially helpful if you are reducing your conventional medication under medical supervision, and believe you would feel more confident, at this transitional stage, by drawing on homoeopathic support. Homoeopathic remedies can also be of great help in dealing with temporary side-effects such as the nausea, diarrhoea or constipation that can sometimes be a feature of taking conventional antidepressants. They can also be very useful as a temporary measure in getting your sleep pattern back on track if you have been having problems with poor-quality or interrupted sleep. If homoeopathic self-help is not proving adequate in managing a problematic situation, always consider seeking professional help from a homoeopathic practitioner.

Greater care needs to be taken with herbal remedies such as St John's Wort. It is not advisable to self-medicate with this herbal preparation if you are already taking a conventional antidepressant, since one may interfere with the medicinal action of the other. On the other hand, if conventional medication has been slowly withdrawn and you feel you need some extra support further down the line for a recurrence of mild to moderate depression, St John's Wort may be an excellent avenue to explore. Apart from potential interaction with antidepressants, further groups of conventional drugs that may have a negative interaction with St John's Wort are outlined in Chapter Seven. On the other hand, simple measures such as using herbal teas in order to reduce anxiety or tension should not cause any problems if you are taking conventional medication.

Aromatherapy can also be a very appropriate avenue to explore if you are taking conventional medication for the treatment of anxiety and depression. This can be especially helpful if you feel you need extra help with relaxation or lifting a general sense of fatigue. Essential oils may be chosen according to their uplifting, soothing or stimulating properties, and may be inhaled, vaporized, added to the bath water or diluted in a carrier oil and massaged on to the skin.

It can also be immensely helpful to boost your progress by taking steps to improve the quality of your daily diet. What you eat and drink can have a powerful positive or negative effect on your body in the long term. See Chapter Six for detailed advice on how you can set about boosting your nutritional status and improving your emotional and mental health at the same time.

Once medication begins to balance your moods, this can be the best time to consider additional improvements in lifestyle that will help you make more positive progress. Ideally these plans should include introducing some form of regular, enjoyable exercise to your daily routine. If anxiety has been a particular problem, it will be very worthwhile to explore relaxation techniques and stress-management strategies that will help protect you from anxiety levels building to a point where they become unmanageable. None of these measures should be regarded as incompatible with taking medication: quite the opposite is true, since positive changes in lifestyle should do a great deal to speed up the rate of overall recovery.

Keeping Self-help Measures within Safe Boundaries

There are certain signs and symptoms that suggest you may be getting out of your depth and need professional help with anxiety and depression:

- the emergence of any indication of symptoms becoming more intense and generally escalating in severity always provides a sign that more professional support needs to be called on. This does not mean that you need to give up on the concept of self-help, but it does strongly suggest that seeking an additional opinion is of paramount importance.
- feelings of being detached or distanced, or a developing sense of unreality in relation to surroundings or people who are familiar to you.
- a developing desire to withdraw from close friends, relatives, or social situations that were previously attractive.
- feelings of grief that refuse to become less intense, even though bereavement may have taken place a long time ago.

- If self-help measures have previously been effective, but appear to have reached an impasse where they are either no longer providing any benefit, or where increasingly large or frequent doses of alternative medicines are being required to maintain a fragile sense of improvement, professional help must be sought from an experienced practitioner. The situation just outlined is a classic indication that the problem has moved beyond the capacities of self-help treatment, and that the home-prescriber is beginning to get out of their depth.
- On no account ever ignore suicidal feelings that may be developing in yourself or expressed by another anxious or depressed person. It is a myth that someone who threatens to commit suicide won't act on these feelings: always err on the side of caution and make sure that these feelings are talked through in a safe, professional context as soon as possible.

Chapter Four

Psychological Approaches

It is very important to bear in mind that you have a great deal of support at your disposal in the form of psychological therapies (sometimes referred to as 'talking' therapies). These may be considered as suitable for patients who have strong reasons for wishing to avoid taking antidepressant medication, or may be used in combination with conventional drug treatments.

Since the potential range of options is very wide and can seem somewhat confusing, it is the aim of this chapter to give a brief and simple description of some of the most common therapies that may be helpful if you suffer from anxiety and depression.

Before we explore some of the basic avenues of psychological help available, it will be helpful to clarify some of the general features that you should be looking for in a therapist if you are going to feel comfortable. Issues for consideration include the following:

- Manner of the therapist. Whatever the nature of the therapy that is being used, it is very important that you should feel comfortable with the person in whom you are putting your trust. As a result, it should be possible to experience a mutual sense of rapport while maintaining a healthy professional distance.
- The surroundings. These should feel appropriately professional, relaxing and free of unwanted distractions. It is essential that you feel comfortable and safe within the space of your sessions.
- Confidence in the therapist. It is very important to feel that a therapist is competent and well within their depth in helping you deal with your problems. After all, you are certain to feel vulnerable and exposed at certain stages of therapy.

In addition, there are certain practical questions you should feel free to ask the therapist, such as:
- How much experience do you have in treating conditions such as mine?

- What qualifications do you have?
- What professional organizations do you belong to?
- Is it possible to predict an approximate time scale for duration of treatment?

Since your main route of referral is going to be through your doctor, questions are unlikely to arise regarding one therapist's advantages over another. Your doctor needs to be trusted to make this decision. However, if you are seeking private therapy sessions, going by the strong recommendation of a friend whose opinion you trust can be the best route to take. If this is not available, self-help organizations may be able to clarify what certain initials and qualifications actually mean.

Psychotherapy

Psychoanalysis
Psychoanalysis is regarded as the expression of psychotherapy in its purest form. Originating in the work of Sigmund Freud, psychoanalysis works from the premise that a large proportion of our mental activity is unconscious, and that emotional problems originate from repressed memories of childhood. Freud attempted to encourage his patients to uncover these buried traumas so that they could integrate these forgotten aspects of their psyche into conscious experience. Freud's approach to the unconscious was generally negative, seeing it as essentially infantile in nature.

It has been suggested that this form of exploratory work is most appropriate for the strongly committed, due to the amount of time and effort that needs to be spent in therapy. On average, if you embark on this avenue of treatment you should expect to be in therapy for approximately two years, during which you will see your therapist five times a week. Clearly this is going to seem daunting to anyone who feels that they need a rapid answer to their mental and emotional distress. As a result, it may be more suitable for someone who is suffering much milder symptoms and who feels that they have the time, financial backing and space within which to embark on such therapy.

During sessions the therapist refrains from revealing a great deal about themselves to their patient, so that it becomes possible for the latter to free-associate and explore past and present relationships which may be a focus of conflict or difficulty. A therapist will often give the impression of being distant, since it is part of their function to say very little. This impression is likely to be made even stronger by the lack of eye contact that is generally involved.

Psychoanalytic Psychotherapy
This is a branch of psychoanalysis which involves a slightly less intense commitment of time, namely one to three sessions a week. Although a couch may be used, as in psychoanalysis, sometimes the patient may sit in a chair facing the therapist.

Analytical Psychology
This is derived from the work of the psychiatrist Carl Jung. In contrast to Freud, Jung viewed the unconscious as being essentially positive in nature. While Freud was more focused on dealing with neurosis, Jung was concerned with personal growth. By virtue of inner exploration, Jung was of the opinion that it is possible to identify a renewed sense of creativity and understanding of the self. Although analytical psychology also works along the lines of releasing unconscious feelings and drives to the conscious level, it brings a more positive perspective to bear on the nature of the unconscious, seeing it as having the potential for containing positive as well as negative elements.

In this form of therapy there is likely to be more active input from the therapist, who may draw on the use of images and drawings in order to gain access to the unconscious. This exploration of the patient's positive potential, although still extremely time-consuming, may appeal to those patients who want to find long-term answers to problems with self-fulfilment.

Transactional Analysis
Transactional analysis was developed by psychiatrist Eric Berne in the 1950s. It has been regarded as a method of therapy that is far more readily accessible than the Freudian approach to psychotherapy. Transactional analysis is concerned with personal development as well as enhancing social functioning. This therapy works from the premise that each of us contains within ourselves three basic states of

experience: the Parent, the Adult, and the Child. A healthy, emotionally balanced person should be able to move freely from one state of response to another, so that one aspect of their personality doesn't move into a dominant position. If the Parent aspect is uppermost, you can find yourself acting as one of your parents would have done in a similar situation, and may even find yourself using learned gestures or phrases from that parent. When your Adult side is in evidence, you are likely to respond effectively and competently to whatever situation you may find yourself presented with. The positive aspects of the Child component can lead to spontaneous, intuitive, refreshing and charming behaviour, but out of balance it can create an unhealthily dependent state.

Transactional analysis can be conducted on a one-to-one or group basis, with therapy sessions occurring once a week.

CognitiveTherapy

This talking therapy is attracting a great deal of attention as a non-drug based way of helping those who suffer from anxiety and depression. Therapists working within this area believe that the way in which people *react* to certain situations affects the way that they feel about them. As a result, if you have a conviction that you are bound to fail when faced with speaking in public, there is every chance that it will go badly. However, if you can change this negative pattern of thinking, you are given the chance of breaking free from a negative vicious circle.

This form of therapy is popular in part because the principles underpinning it can be quickly accessed and understood, and, unlike psychoanalysis, it does not necessitate getting involved in intensive therapy that can involve years of work and exploration. However, it is worth pointing out that while this approach may work extremely well for some patients who are anxious or depressed, the exploration of patterns of behaviour from the past can sometimes feel uncomfortable or confrontational rather than positively liberating. As always, this depends on the individual's mental and emotional make-up: what may be extremely appropriate for one may be unsuitable for another.

BehaviourTherapy

This may be a useful option for those who have phobias that can lead to the avoidance of certain situations. While this may not greatly affect their lives (for instance if they have phobias of scorpions or snakes), severe anxiety symptoms that are set off by a fear of being away from home or in large groups of people can have a severely compromising effect, making the circle of possibilities open to them increasingly narrow. It is the aim of behaviour therapy to allow you to overcome the feelings of increasing terror that are sparked off by situations you might opt out of if given the opportunity.

If you choose to see a behaviour therapist, they will encourage you to describe the specific fears and phobias that are limiting your day-to-day experience. They will then ask you to imagine the situation you are wary of, while you practise conscious relaxation. In time, the goal is to get you to confront the situations you have been avoiding, accompanied by the therapist or a friend or relative whom you trust. By breaking through the barrier in this way it is thought that you can gradually dismantle the often irrational feelings of fear that surround the experience. Avoidance, sadly, can never allow you to make this progress.

Behaviour therapy may be used on its own merits, or it can be used in combination with medication, depending on the needs of the patient. Do remember that you are not limited to using conventional medication to give you the additional support you are likely to need when confronting an anxiety-making situation, since some of the alternative approaches discussed in Chapter Seven can also provide you with a great deal of additional practical help.

Counselling

You can benefit from counselling if you are concerned about specific issues that are causing you unhappiness or dissatisfaction in your life (as in the case of couples' counselling, family counselling or grief counselling). Alternatively, you may seek counselling as a general form of supportive therapy if you feel that your problems are affecting you on a more global basis. It has been suggested that if people have difficulties that are affecting a *part* of their lives they should see a counsellor, while if they have problems that are affecting the *whole* of their lives they should consult a psychotherapist. However, this suggestion can be rather simplistic and more than a little misleading.

There are many different forms of counselling, some taking a non-directive approach and others working with specific, more directive techniques. Whatever its orientation, effective counselling should ideally empower the client to discover inner resources on which to draw in order to live life in a more satisfying and rewarding way.

A counsellor should be able to listen to their clients in an objective way, so that they are able to understand what is being said, without the obstacle of their own emotional response getting in the way. This does not mean that a counsellor cannot be empathetic and approachable, merely that they will be working within disciplined parameters, rather than allowing the session to drift along the lines of a conversation with a friend.

Counselling can be applied on a short-term basis for a situation of immediate crisis, or on a long-term basis in order to enable the client to identify more deep-seated areas of conflict and difficulty, so that positive change becomes possible.

Hypnotherapy and Meditation

These are techniques that can be used to calm the mind by focusing intently on an object, sound or bodily sensation. As a result of this profound sense of concentration, other intruding worries, anxieties and distracting thoughts recede into the background. In this trance-like state, it is possible to be open to positive suggestions, but it is a myth that you can be forced to carry out any action under the power of hypnosis that is against your conscious will.

Light hypnosis can be combined with psychotherapy in order to enable memories to be retrieved from the unconscious. Under hypnosis it may be possible to draw on memories that pre-date conscious recollections. It may also be possible to access feelings that have been repressed from the conscious mind.

Both hypnotherapy and meditation can be powerful aids to deep relaxation. Anxiety-related problems such as panic attacks, high blood pressure and tension headaches often respond positively to hypnosis or meditation.

However, although hypnotherapy and meditation are generally very safe, advice must be sought in cases of deep or very severe depression and/or anxiety, especially if symptoms appear to be aggravated by the practice of auto-hypnosis or meditation. In such cases, the evaluation and professional support of an experienced therapist is invaluable.

Chapter Five

Complementary and Alternative Treatments

Alternative and complementary medicines are hot news these days. This is reflected in the way in which it is very rare not to see a section on the alternative viewpoint in any discussion of topical health issues in the popular press. This is especially true of a newsworthy subject such as depression, since this is a problem that previously was seldom openly discussed. With the advent of controversial conventional antidepressants such as Prozac, and the growing recognition that counselling, psychological and psychotherapeutic support can be of tremendous value in helping someone come to terms with an underlying predisposition to depression and anxiety, some of the previous stigma that has been associated with mental illness has, thankfully, been eroded. This is surely fairly inevitable when we consider the magnitude of depressive illness as a modern problem, which so many people appear to be struggling with. This was reflected in a recent report, which suggested that as many as a staggering one in three British people are currently diagnosed as suffering from depression.

In addition, consciousness of the positive potential of alternative and complementary therapies has increased and developed as a result of the boom in self-help literature which first appeared in the 1980s. As a consequence, many people have responded very positively to the idea that they can use simple, effective natural medicines and methods of healing in order to deal with straightforward, acute, self-limiting conditions at home.

As an extension of this approach, it also became clear that more chronic, recurring, well-established conditions such as eczema, hay fever, irritable bowel syndrome, migraines and tension headaches could respond effectively to professional treatment by a practitioner of an appropriate alternative therapy.

Even more significantly for the purposes of this book, it has emerged that alternative and complementary approaches can play an important role in treating, or considerably alleviating, conditions which can cause a great deal of mental and emotional distress, such as anxiety and depression. The alternative and complementary approach appears to possess a particular potential for treating conditions of this kind, due to the importance these therapies attribute to the state of emotional and mental health in any assessment of the overall health of the patient.

The Whole Picture

Alternative therapists such as homoeopaths tend to regard emotional and mental problems as indicative of the whole system being out of balance. This is why patients may sometimes be surprised when they consult an alternative therapist about their skin, chest, or bowel problems, and find that they spend as much time exploring their emotional and mental state as they do describing their physical symptoms.

This exploration of emotional and mental equilibrium is central to the whole body/mind approach to alternative treatment, since most patients with severe or persistent physical ailments are also in a state of emotional and mental discomfort. More often than not, physical symptoms can arise during or following a period of protracted stress, or shock, so that the disturbance may be seen to have originated from an emotional reaction to a distressing or unsettling situation. Occasionally, alternative therapists may be faced with depressive or anxious problems that emerge when a protracted physical ailment refuses to improve or clear up, regardless of any number of conventional medicines that may have been tried. This can be especially true of visible skin conditions, which have an undermining effect on self-esteem or confidence, or physical ailments which drain basic levels of energy and vitality or have a negative effect on the patient's social life (such as irritable bowel syndrome or migraines).

The beauty of the alternative and complementary approach is that it doesn't matter which way round problems with anxiety and depression have developed, because alternative therapies attempt to the stimulate the *whole system* into an optimum state of balance and harmony. As a result, once treatment is seen to be effective, emotional and mental balance improves, with a corresponding improvement in energy levels. Once greater psychological equilibrium has become established, it is very common for physical problems to clear up. This is especially noticeable with regard to physical ailments that have been aggravated by stress. As you begin to unwind and feel more positive in response to alternative medical approaches, you are also likely to feel empowered and inspired to take the stress-management steps you may have previously felt unable to take.

In addition, alternative and complementary approaches have a significant factor in their favour with regard to their general lack of side-effects. This is in sharp contrast to some conventional drugs, which can have drawbacks associated with them. To be fair, some of the side-effects of conventional medicines may be minor and are known to disappear or improve with continued use, but it must be said that other side-effects may make continuing with the medication unappealing or positively unacceptable. In such a situation, help from an alternative or complementary medical source may be something that can be of particular value and support.

What These Therapies Have to Offer

Before we consider the practical application of any non-conventional approach, it will be extremely helpful to clarify exactly what is meant by 'alternative' and 'complementary' treatments. In reality these form part of a continuous spectrum, with therapies that provide complete systems of healing which offer genuine alternatives to conventional medicines at one end, and therapies that can be effectively used side by side with conventional treatment at the other.

There is no hard-and-fast wisdom that has been handed down on this somewhat controversial subject, and there may well be representatives of various therapies who might disagree with what follows. However, for practical purposes it helps to separate those systems of healing that are complete in themselves from those that can be regarded as having more limited application. This is not done in order to suggest that the latter are inferior in any way, but just to clarify that they may not be able to provide as much flexible and immediate support within a challenging therapeutic context.

Viewed from within this context, complete systems of healing that are readily available include Western medical herbalism, traditional Chinese medicine (including acupuncture and Chinese herbal medicines), and homoeopathy. In addition, Ayurvedic and Anthroposophical medicine also provide complete systems of healing, but tend to be less practically accessible (for example, finding a practitioner may not be so easy).

Systems of healing that may be called upon to provide help in more complementary or adjunctive contexts may include any of the following extremely popular therapies: reflexology, acupressure, osteopathy, chiropractic, aromatherapy, Shiatsu, Indian head massage, Bach flower essences or hypnotherapy. From considering this last list, you may make the general observation that more adjunctive, complementary therapies tend to fall into the 'hands-on' category, where the more major systems which can be applied within an alternative context use medicines that have a flexible and potentially wide sphere of application.

Having said this, the picture is not quite so clear-cut as it might first seem, since some alternative systems of healing can be used in a complementary way (for instance, using traditional Chinese medicine side by side with conventional treatment, or using homoeopathic medicines within a self-help context for acute problems). This is an extremely positive point, since it allows for an important degree of flexibility of use for the patient. No one should find themselves boxed-in by feeling they have to make a stark choice between an alternative or conventional medical approach.

Most alternative therapists should take the line that, if it is possible to improve health problems using effective methods of healing that are gentler on the system, this clearly provides a huge advantage. However, if this has not proved possible, or if a patient is already committed to a long-term course of medication that cannot under any circumstances be safely stopped (and this may be the case in severe cases of clinical depression or agitated anxiety), there is still a great deal to be offered by providing additional support in the form of complementary treatment.

Having established some general boundaries within which alternative and complementary medicines can be used, we now need to consider how this may be done with the maximum amount of safety and security for patients suffering from depression and anxiety.

Generally speaking, an alternative approach to treating those who suffer from problems with anxiety and depression is going to yield the most positive results in mild to moderate cases. This is especially the case for anyone attempting to handle their situation with self-help measures, since severe cases demand professional support in order to ensure the most positive outcome within a secure context. On the other hand, if someone has no established history of emotional problems, but has experienced short, mild episodes of anxiety and/or depression, effective self-help measures may be enough to rectify the situation. If after a while sufficient improvement is not forthcoming, it would be wise to consult an alternative practitioner, who will be in a better position to make an objective assessment of the situation.

People suffering from moderate cases of anxiety and depression may respond especially well to an alternative approach if they have previously responded well to conventional medical help, but now want to find ways of improving their overall mental, emotional and physical resilience and equilibrium. Some patients with a moderate level of anxiety and depression may also benefit from alternative approaches if they are coming off their medication (always with the supervision and consent of their doctor or therapist), but feel that they need extra support from an alternative route.

In severe cases of anxiety and depression, greater care must be taken because of the potential seriousness of the conditions, and the major disruption that may be caused by any form of intervention that is not considered and evaluated carefully. This is due to the nature of the medication that may be used. For instance, the drug Lithium may be prescribed in very severe depressive states, and should *never* be withdrawn abruptly without medical supervision. This is also true of antidepressants that have been used for an extended period of time. If withdrawal is considered a viable option, it should never be embarked upon without adequate medical supervision and assessment. However, this does not suggest that complementary approaches cannot play a role within the context of treating severe anxiety and depression. Indeed, they can be very helpful as additional methods of support.

Appropriate use of complementary therapies can help reduce the distress of side-effects caused by conventional medicines, while also stimulating improved energy levels and well-being through enhanced relaxation. When nutritional approaches are explored there is also the bonus of elevated nutritional status, something that is of particular benefit to those who suffer from depression. This is due to the way in which those who have suffered from severe or well-established depressive illness often neglect the quality of what they eat due to reduced motivation and lack of self-esteem.

Combining Complementary Approaches with Conventional Medication

As suggested above, there should be very few obstacles in your way if you wish to combine alternative therapies with conventional medication. Homoeopathic remedies can be used, without risk, side by side with conventional treatment, as can acupuncture and some Western or Chinese herbal medicines. However, care needs to be taken when using a small number of herbal preparations, since some of these may interact adversely with specific orthodox medication, or may render some conventional drugs inactive. For more information on this subject see the section on St John's Wort in Chapter Seven (page 85).

If you have any doubts about interactions between any herbal preparation and conventional medication, it may be helpful initially to speak to your doctor. If he or she has no knowledge or experience of the herbal medicine involved, your next step should be to seek the advice of a pharmacist.

Therapies such as aromatherapy, reflexology, chiropractic, osteopathy, acupuncture, Shiatsu or acupressure should not pose any problems when used in combination with conventional drugs, and may do a great deal to relieve the symptoms of discomfort and pain which can arise in association with mental, emotional and physical tension.

When You Might Want to Consult an Alternative Medical Practitioner

There are certain specific pointers that suggest you may be getting out of your depth with home-prescribing. In general, these can apply to any condition that is showing signs of deteriorating, but the following advice has been tailored to describe situations that can arise when attempting effective, self-help management of mild cases of anxiety and depression. Always seek advice from a trained practitioner if any of the following occur:

- indications that suggest that symptoms are getting more severe and disruptive (for instance, finding work or maintaining relationships is becoming increasingly difficult and stressful).
- a recurrence of anxiety or depression in anyone who has a previous history of a severe episode that required professional support and treatment.
- any sign that suggests that more frequent or higher doses of alternative medication are needed in order to keep symptoms at bay.
- the emergence of symptoms that are resistant to self-help treatment. This does not automatically suggest that alternative therapies are inappropriate, but that self-help measures have not been sufficiently effective in improving the situation.
- any confusion or doubt about how to proceed with self-help measures.

Chapter Six

Nutritional Self-help

Few people can be unaware of the importance of sound nutrition these days. Messages are constantly being communicated via the popular press, television and the internet focusing on the need to take advantage of high-quality nutrition if you are to have the best chance of enjoying maximum health and vitality. While discussions of the basic importance of sound nutrition often relate to the promotion of a sense of physical well-being, it is also increasingly acknowledged that poor-quality nutritional status can have a major effect on mental and emotional health.

The issue of nutrition is also of particular interest in any consideration of the treatment of anxiety and depression, since specific foods and drinks are known to play a part in either aggravating or alleviating symptoms of these conditions. As a result, you can improve your situation at a basic, practical level if you pay attention to improving the quality of your day-to-day eating patterns. By doing so you are also giving yourself the best chance of easing the troublesome digestive problems that so often accompany anxiety and depression, as well as associated symptoms of insomnia and fatigue.

Many people may have heard the phrase 'you are what you eat' and dismissed it as trite and too obvious for consideration. However, it is worth pausing for a moment and thinking about the implications of this simple statement. You are dependent on the food and drink that you ingest for providing the body with the basic building blocks it requires for repair and renewal, as well as providing the essential fuel that is burned to give you heat and energy. As a result, the quality of your basic diet plays a crucially important role in determining how your body functions at a fundamental cellular level. The quality of your nutritional status also plays a pivotal part in supporting your immune system and protecting against vitamin, mineral or trace-element deficiencies that can lead to symptoms of anaemia or recurrent infections.

Foods to Avoid when Anxious or Depressed

The following should be avoided whenever possible, or cut down dramatically if you are subject to recurrent bouts of anxiety or depression. It is worth pointing out that these items are, paradoxically, the very things that we often crave when we are feeling low or anxious. As a result, we can find ourselves unwittingly in the grip of a vicious circle, craving the very foods and drinks that are aggravating our symptoms. The good news, however, is that once you begin to change your eating and drinking habits by making positive adjustments, you are likely to find that your mood is more stable and balanced, while your overall health is likely to benefit as well.

Foods and Drinks Containing Refined Sugar

Unstable blood sugar levels can make mood changes, jitteriness, irritability, headaches, depression and general lightheadedness more severe. As a result, you should make reducing the amount of white (refined) sugar in your diet a priority. Not only does a high intake of sugar in the form of cakes, biscuits, puddings, sweets, convenience foods and fizzy drinks contribute to blood sugar highs and lows, but it can also lead to a wide range of additional problems in the form of weight gain, dental cavities and, when high-sugar foods are combined with generous portions of saturated fat in the form of pastries, cream cakes and puddings, an increased risk of heart disease. For a more detailed account of how to balance blood sugar, see the section below on foods and drinks that stabilize blood sugar (page 75).

Caffeinated Foods and Drinks

These, which include coffees, teas, colas, high-energy drinks and chocolate, fall into a broadly addictive category, which may make it difficult for you to contemplate giving them up, or even reducing your intake considerably. However, if you take the plunge you can do yourself a huge favour in the general health stakes, before you even consider the advantages that come from improved emotional balance. Caffeine, when taken on a regular basis, leads to problems with jitteriness, increased anxiety, insomnia, palpitations and a tendency to sharp mood swings. Additional problems associated with the regular use of caffeine include fatigue, unstable blood sugar levels, and increased risk of developing osteoporosis (brittle bones).

Alcohol
Alcohol brings many problems in its wake, since it can have a depressant effect, making a low mood even more distressing. In addition, alcohol can result in disturbed or unrefreshing sleep, digestive disorders, poor absorption of essential vitamins and minerals, osteoporosis and liver problems.

Convenience Foods
Convenience or 'instant' meals can be immensely helpful when time is in short supply and we need a quick way of putting a meal together. However, if we get into the habit of relying almost exclusively on 'quick-fix' foods that are frozen, vacuum-packed or dehydrated to meet our nutritional requirements, we are going to have problems in the long run. This is even more likely to be the case if we feel stressed and under pressure, since our need for soundly-nutritious food increases at this time. Apart from a generally poor nutritional status, specific problems that may emerge in response to a diet that relies too heavily on junk food may include allergic symptoms, high blood pressure, fatigue, digestive discomfort, erratic blood sugar levels and weight gain. Since junk foods are also extremely likely to be a poor supply of the essential vitamins and minerals we need if we are suffering from depression or anxiety (such as the B-complex vitamins, which support the nervous system), an imbalanced diet can lead to further problems.

Cigarettes
Although they are of course not a food, cigarettes also need to be drawn into any discussion of lifestyle factors which may aggravate or alleviate problems with depression. Apart from the additional health problems which appear to be linked with cigarette smoking, such as bronchitis, lung cancer, osteoporosis, heart disease and signs of premature ageing, there are more specific drawbacks in relation to depressive illness. It has been estimated that smokers are three times more likely to suffer from depression than those who don't smoke if other co-factors are also pesent.

Foods to Concentrate on when Anxious or Depressed

If you suffer from anxiety or depression, you should be aiming to make the following foods basic elements of your diet. Not only are there wide-ranging health benefits to be gained from taking these broad principles on board, but the mood-balancing potential of this way of eating is too important to miss if you are vulnerable to anxiety or depression. There's absolutely no need to get hung up on feeling that this is a restrictive or strict way of eating, since what is being suggested is that you should be aiming just to change the *balance* of your diet in favour of a more nutritionally sound basis. As a result, you should look on this exercise as a way of adding extra nutritious food to your daily eating plans, rather than concentrating on excluding less-than-healthy items.

Complex Carbohydrates
These include whole grains (in the form of bread or pasta), potatoes, and vegetables. Since complex carbohydrates take longer to be broken down than simple sugars, they give you a more sustained energy release and also benefit your mood. This is thought to be due to the way in which complex carbohydrates can boost serotonin levels in the brain. Serotonin is a neurotransmitter that is known to have an anti depressant effect. In addition, complex carbohydrates appear to have an anxiety-reducing effect, leaving you feeling calmed and less jittery. Fringe health benefits of a diet that is high in complex carbohydrates include a reduced tendency to fatigue, smoother digestive functioning, and reduced risk of constipation.

Filtered or Still Mineral Water
Many people walk around experiencing a low level of dehydration which they are completely unaware of. Niggling symptoms such as sluggishness, constipation, muzzy-headedness and recurrent headaches can all be related to an on-going state of dehydration. The problem may be unwittingly aggravated by drinking tea and coffee, since we may mistakenly believe these can also be counted as contributing towards our fluid intake. Apart from the negative effect on emotional balance that these drinks can have, as outlined in the section above, they also bring additional problems with them since they have a diuretic effect. This means that they stimulate the body to excrete more fluid, which can further contribute to a mildly dehydrated

state. Making sure that you have approximately five large glasses of water a day *in addition* to any other fluids that you drink is one of the most effective ways of guarding against dehydration. Spread these throughout the course of the day, making sure that you take a bottle of water to work so that you can assess, by the end of the day, how much water you have actually drunk.

Herbal Teas and Coffee Substitutes
These days you should have very few problems when it comes to finding palatable alternatives to coffee and tea. Gone are the days when all that could be found was dandelion coffee; you can now choose between fruit-flavoured or a wide range of caffeine-free herbal teas. If you prefer the flavour of a milky coffee, you may enjoy one of the many powdered or granulated coffee substitutes that are available. In addition, green tea is gathering increasing attention as a hot beverage that is refreshing but also brings positive health benefits in the form of immune-system-boosting anti-oxidant nutrients. None of these drinks should make you feel jittery, while some herbal teas, such as camomile, will help induce a calmer state of mind, and may help you gain a restful night's sleep if you have a tendency to a poor sleep pattern.

Foods Rich in B Vitamins
It is worth making sure that you have regular helpings of the following foods, since they are sources of B vitamins: nuts, whole grains, dark green leafy vegetables, fish, yeast extract, bananas, brown rice, and products made from soya flour. You need support from the B vitamin group whenever you are stressed and low, since they play an important role in maintaining the health and resilience of the immune system.

Blood Sugar Levels

As suggested above, it is essential to pay attention to stabilizing blood sugar levels as much as possible if you suffer from anxiety and depression. This is because many features of low blood sugar (hypoglycaemia) overlap with symptoms of anxiety and depression, and can aggravate the situation further. Once you have identified how this works you are in a liberating position, since you can take the practical steps outlined below to improve the situation.

Possible symptoms that may be associated with hypoglycaemia may include any of the following: headaches, drowsiness, irritability, lack of concentration, panicky sensations, depression, chest pain, palpitations, trembling, food cravings, loss of libido, and general aches and pains.

Some might mistakenly think that all you should do to guard against low blood sugar levels is to make sure that you eat lots of sweet food and drinks, and add in some extras that are known to raise blood sugar, such as coffee or alcohol. Unfortunately, this is the very worst thing you could employ as a long-term strategy, since it is sure to make the overall situation worse.

Feeding yourself refined sugar over-stimulates the production of insulin, which *lowers* blood sugar levels. The organ responsible for regulating blood sugar levels is the pancreas, and there is a danger, if you eat too much sugar for too long, that you will end up with a trigger-happy, and eventually exhausted pancreas. As a result of eating regular quantities of refined carbohydrates made from white sugar and white flour, blood sugar levels rise dramatically, with the rapid response of the pancreas being to secrete insulin to bring blood sugar levels down. Once this happens, you move into a situation of low blood sugar levels and are likely to respond by craving something sweet in order to give yourself a further energy boost. As you can see, this leads to the vicious circle where you are on a blood sugar roller coaster that is likely to do nothing for your state of mind or energy levels.

Foods and Drinks that Stabilize Blood Sugar

There are two factors to bear in mind regarding keeping blood sugar levels stable: the nature of the food you eat, and the regularity with which you eat it. Foods that should be cut down on, or cut out of the diet completely, include table sugar, sweets, white bread, chocolate, cakes, biscuits, alcohol, pastries, fizzy colas, fruit squashes and any form of junk food that is unrecognizable from its natural state (in other words, if it has been supplemented with sweeteners, preservatives or artificial colourings. A good example would be tinned tomato soup, which bears very little relationship to home-made tomato soup in terms of sweetness, colour or texture).

Also be aware that it is best to avoid low-calorie convenience foods and drinks when attempting to stabilize blood sugar levels. Because these are low in sugar, you might mistakenly think that they are a healthy alternative to sugar-laden foods or drinks. Sadly, these items bring their own problems in their wake, in the guise of a hefty proportion of chemical sweeteners, artificial flavourings and preservatives. Taken together, these form a chemical cocktail that is unlikely to contribute to a healthy diet.

Instead of 'no-calorie' or 'low-calorie' items, concentrate instead on including plenty of complex, unrefined carbohydrates in the form of potatoes, grains, bread and vegetables, and have regular portions of fresh fruit. Although the latter contain their own form of sugar, called fructose, it is buffered by the fibre that is to be found in the fruit. As a result, the sugar enters the bloodstream more slowly than it would in the form of fruit juice, and certainly a lot more slowly than it would in the form of convenience foods, which contain a large percentage of sucrose (table sugar). When choosing drinks, opt wherever possible for sparkling or still mineral water, with a little fresh fruit juice occasionally added for variety's sake. Also have plenty of hot drinks in the form of unsweetened herbal or fruit teas, or coffee substitutes.

The basic items you should be aiming to include as staple features of your diet include the following: whole-grain products such as wholemeal bread, pasta, brown rice, and oats. You should also include nuts, seeds, peas, beans, lentils, vegetables and fresh fruit. If you are not vegetarian, a small amount of animal protein may be included in the form of cheese, eggs, poultry, milk and yoghurt. Regular portions of red meat are generally best avoided if you are concerned about looking after your health, since the saturated fat concentration to be found in red meat can elevate your risk of developing heat disease. If you really can't contemplate giving up red meat, it's best to opt for organic produce, since this enables you to avoid problems with antibiotic and growth-hormone residues, which can be a problem with non-organic meat.

Although there is a strong vogue at the moment for low-fat products, you should take care how you reduce fat in your day-to-day eating patterns. While it is certainly true that most people eat far too high a proportion of unhealthy fat on a regular basis, you need to consider that there are some forms of fat that can be positively beneficial when eaten in small quantities each day. These are to be found in virgin, cold-pressed olive oil, and unrefined sunflower oil. The fat to be found in oily fish also appears to play an important role in protecting the health of your heart and circulatory system, while essential fatty acids may also obtained from fresh vegetables and nuts.

Saturated fats should be eaten very sparingly, since they do appear to leave us vulnerable to developing heart disease and breast cancer. Saturated fats are solid at room temperature and include items such as butter, full-fat cheeses, cream, some margarines and lard.

If you are seeking to guard against problems with low blood sugar, the following should be avoided whenever possible: sugar, sweets, alcohol, junk foods, sugary drinks, chocolate, biscuits, white bread, white pasta, puddings and sweet pastries.

Chapter Seven

Herbs, Homoeopathy and Aromatherapy

The general value of an alternative and complementary approach in treating anxiety and depression has already been discussed in Chapter Five. It is now time to examine some of these therapies in more detail, so that you can gain a basic grasp of what to expect if you decide to seek treatment from a trained practitioner In addition we will explore how herbal and homoeopathic medicines and aromatherapy may be applied within a self-help context.

Herbal Medicine

Herbal medicine can be broadly divided into two branches: Western medical herbalism and Chinese herbal medicine.

Western Medical Herbalism

Herbalism has a great deal in common with other alternative medical systems. This common ground includes the basic belief that the human organism possesses an in-built, self-regulating and self-healing mechanism that strives to keep mind, emotions and body in as positive a state of equilibrium as possible. This fundamental capacity for adapting and adjusting can be seen in the way that the human body can respond appropriately and rapidly to changes in external temperature. When this equilibrium is maintained, we feel in a state of optimum health. However, should this fundamental sense of harmony move into a state of disarray for any extended period of time, we are likely to feel generally unwell, or may go on to develop specific symptoms of an identifiable illness.

Western medical herbalism has a long and established history, with a body of knowledge being developed in a practical way, on a trial-and-error basis over many years. It may surprise you to discover that conventional doctors rely on a high proportion of drugs that are derived from plant sources; however the methods of preparation of conventional drugs is quite different to the way in which the same plant may be used by a medical herbalist. When conventional drugs are manufactured, the emphasis is put on developing concentrated, measurable amounts of the ingredient within the plant that is seen to have an active effect. This clearly has some practical advantages (such as the ability to work with finely measured doses of an ingredient that is seen to be pharmacologically active). However, when a more holistic perspective is adopted we can begin to appreciate the disadvantages of concentrating isolated chemical compounds of a plant for medicinal purposes.

Herbalists believe that there are perceptible advantages to be gained from using medicines that are derived from the *whole* plant, as opposed to a concentrated extract, advantages linked to the balanced effects as the medicinal effects of one chemical compound of the plant act as a buffer against another.

You can see this process in action if you take the simple example of the development of the drug aspirin. Originally obtained from a natural plant source, it was discovered that the drug which came to be known as aspirin (acetylsalicylic acid) could be isolated, concentrated and used as a very effective pain-reliever. However, it emerged that using the drug in this way on a long-term basis could lead to stomach irritation and bleeding.

Herbalists also make use of the same substance, but by making use of the whole plant a different, less toxic effect is produced. This is due to the way in which the salicylate content of the plant acts as an effective anti-inflammatory and pain-reliever, while the tannin and soothing mucilage content also to be found in the same plant source act as important buffers, discouraging stomach bleeding and irritation.

As you can see, the beneficial, medicinal potential of plants is quite complex, with the effect of the whole plant being much more than the sum of the chemical effects of its individual parts.

It has also been suggested that the more balanced, buffering effect to be found by using whole plants – rather than isolated, concentrated ingredients helps guard against the risk of the emergence of toxic side-effects . This is something that is recognized as a perceptible risk when using powerful conventional drugs such as steroids and lithium. When drugs of these kinds are used in high dosage on a long-term basis, responsible monitoring must be carried out in order to ensure that undesirable side-effects do not damage vital organs such as the kidneys, adrenal glands, and those that make up the immune system.

If you consult a Western medical herbalist you can expect to have a very thorough examination. Detailed information will be gathered about your general quality of life, diet and stress levels. Questions are also likely to be asked about whether you have any digestive, respiratory or circulatory problems. Your pulse and blood pressure may be taken, and a physical examination may also be conducted. Some herbalists may also use iridology as an additional diagnostic tool. This involves examining the flecks and patterns within the iris of your eye, as a method of establishing whether there may be weaknesses or problems within specific areas or organs of the body.

Once this information has been assimilated and analysed by the herbalist, a programme of treatment can begin. This will usually take the form of a prescription of appropriate herbs to attempt to stimulate the self-healing mechanism of the body. The aim is to promote an overall improved state of balance in the body, by tailoring the herbs prescribed to meet your individual needs. In some cases this will involve the use of herbs which have specific anti-inflammatory properties or antibiotic properties, while others may require the use of herbs which have tonic, stimulant or relaxant qualities.

In addition to whichever herbal prescription is made, you may also be given advice on appropriate adjustments that are likely to support a move towards improved health. This could involve recommendations about exercise and/or relaxation techniques, and advice on dietary improvements or breathing techniques which can help your body eliminate toxins more efficiently.

Chinese Herbal Medicine

When you consult a Chinese herbalist you are likely to be struck by the amount of keen observation that the practitioner employs. This involves examination of your tongue, which is regarded as revealing a great deal about the nature of your overall health. Reading the pulse is also of pivotal importance in reaching a diagnosis, with certain qualities, such as the pulse's strength, frequency and regularity, being evaluated.

In addition, the nature and tone of your voice will be taken into account, since this can reveal additional informtion about your state of mind. After all, many of us may find that our voices modify and change when we are feeling tense, anxious, hesitant, unconfident or depressed. Since Chinese herbalists employ a holistic perspective – with treatment being aimed at improving the total experience of health on mental, emotional and physical levels – clues which may point to emotional imbalance can be of particular value and significance to the practitioner.

After reaching a diagnosis, a Chinese herbal practitioner will select a prescription of herbs, which may come in the form of pills, powders or liquids. You might even be given a mixture of dried herbs to be simmered in a pan of water, strained off and drunk (this is called a *decoction*). Pills or capsules may be chosen for their convenience, or for patients who find the taste of a decoction too off-putting to continue with treatment. Some practitioners of traditional Chinese medicine may combine acupuncture with herbal treatment in an effort to stimulate the body, mind and emotions towards a state of improved balance, health and vitality.

Homoeopathic Medicine

Homoeopathy is a popular, gentle, effective method of healing. Like herbalism, it attempts to stimulate mind, emotions and body towards an optimum state of harmony and balance. When homoeopathic treatment is effective, not only should troublesome physical symptoms improve, but there should also be a corresponding improvement in mental and emotional well-being. Many patients also find, to their delight, that they experience restored levels of energy and vitality.

Unlike herbalism, which has such a long and extended history of use, homoeopathy is a relative youngster on the alternative scene, with a track record of approximately 200 years. Originally developed as a gentle system of healing that would avoid the pitfalls of the conventional medical practices of the time – with their drastic methods of treatment such as poisoning, bleeding, and purging – homoeopathy was born out of a desire to restore patients to health in the most effective and humane, and least traumatic way, as possible.

The founder of homoeopathic medicine was a German doctor called Samuel Hahnemann, who became increasingly disturbed by the harsh reality of conventional medical treatment of his day. Relatively early in his medical career, Hahnemann became convinced that he was doing more harm than good for his patients, and gave up the practice of orthodox medicine. He conducted an extended series of experiments using increasingly diluted medicines, until he developed the system of healing that has come to be known as homoeopathy.

Homoeopathic medicines are quite different to conventional drugs in two ways. The first concerns their highly diluted nature: to a point where there are unlikely to be any molecules of the original substance left in any given dose. The second issue is linked to the concept of similars. As we know, most conventional drugs work by opposing whatever bodily process appears to be causing a problem. As a result, conventional doctors will prescribe anti-inflammatories to reduce inflammation and pain, laxatives for constipation, and antibiotics in order to combat a bacterial infection.

Homoeopaths, on the other hand, prescribe medicines that have a *similar* rather than *opposite* effect. In other words, substances are used that would *cause* disease symptoms in a healthy person when given in a non-diluted dose over an extended period of time. These same substances appear to work therapeutically when given to a sick person in the form of a tiny, energized dose, provided the symptoms experienced by the patient closely resemble those known to be produced by the substance that has been given.

When this match is as accurate as it can be, the homoeopathic remedy appears to act as a catalyst, 'kick-starting' the self-healing mechanism of the body. However, if a totally unsuitable remedy is given (i.e. one that bears little resemblance to the characteristic symptoms of the patient), nothing is likely to happen.

The ultimate importance of matching the individual symptoms of the patient to the most appropriate remedy (rather like finding the perfect match between a key and a lock), is the rationale behind the detailed and lengthy nature of a first consultation with a homoeopathic practitioner. This can take anything up to an hour and a half, and during the course of this interview the homoeopath is likely to ask all sorts of questions that will enable them to grasp a sense of what makes each individual patient 'tick'. Questions may be asked about your ability to deal with stress, your energy levels, zest for life, quality of sleep, resistance to infection and overall ability to concentrate, as well as detailed questions about the main medical problem that led you to seek homoeopathic treatment. A detailed medical history will also be taken, as well as information about the medical history of your close relatives.

Once all of this information has been gathered to the satisfaction of the homoeopath, it is time to do a case analysis in order to work out which homoeopathic remedy is likely to match your characteristic symptoms most snugly. This work may be done using a textbook called a *repertory*, and another called a *materia medica*, though, increasingly, homoeopaths of today will make use of computer programmes to make analysis much faster and more efficient.

The appropriate remedy may be given in a range of different forms, depending on what is most appropriate for each patient. These could include tablets, powders, liquids or granules, with some patients taking their remedy three or four times a day, while others may take a single dose of one or two tablets. Patients may be instructed to observe their reactions to the dose over the following two to three weeks.

Many patients are surprised and delighted when they discover that successful homoeopathic treatment does not involve being dependent on taking homoeopathic remedies on a long-term or permanent basis. Homoeopathic remedies, when accurately prescribed, act as catalysts for the self-regulating mechanism of the body, encouraging it to act effectively and decisively. Once this has been set firmly in motion, no further homoeopathic support may be needed. This process can take weeks, months or sometimes years to occur, depending on your vitality, constitution, age and susceptibility to treatment.

Aromatherapy

Aromatherapy is an extremely popular and flexible therapy which draws on the healing properties of essential oils. Aromatherapists are trained to provide treatment for patients who may be suffering from a wide range of chronic conditions, such as tension headaches, migraines, sleep problems, skin disorders such as eczema or psoriasis, and stress-related conditions. When an aromatherapist is trained they are required to develop a detailed understanding of the medicinal properties of essential oils, as well as having a grasp of how the body works through a basic training in anatomy and physiology.

Aromatherapy is also a very popular choice for self-help purposes because of the ready availability of essential oils, and the simply pleasurable aspect of a therapy that is based on the sensuous principle of smell.

However, it has been suggested that those of us who want to experiment with the use of essential oils at home should ideally have first attended an introductory course on the practical use of aromatherapy oils. This is done for basic reasons of safety of use, and in order to encourage the greatest accuracy and precision when deciding on which essential oils should be selected for any condition being treated at home.

When you consult an aromatherapist you should be prepared to go through a basic case history which will explore the quality of health you experience on a mental, emotional and physical level. After considering this information, the aromatherapist will select a blend of essential oils that will be tailored to meet your individual requirements. The blend is likely to be applied to your skin in the form of an aromatherapy massage, or it may also be recommended for inhalation. Although some aromatherapists on the Continent may suggest that aromatherapy oils may be ingested for medicinal purposes, this is something that is not generally advocated in Britain, and certainly never for the self-prescriber experimenting at home.

Aromatherapy is regarded as a holistic treatment, with a skilled and experienced therapist attempting to elevate the overall health of the patient, rather than targeting the piecemeal treatment of individual symptoms. Because the whole picture is being attended to, some time may be devoted in the initial consultation to exploring issues of diet, exercise, sleep quality and general stress-management.

If we take the simple example of someone suffering from muscle aches and tension, a blend of oils especially appropriate for soothing tight muscle tissue may be massaged into the affected area. The soothing effect of this 'hands-on' treatment can be further enhanced by educating the patient in ways of reducing stress and tension, such as taking up a relaxation technique, attending a yoga class and avoiding or reducing foods and drinks that are known to have a negative effect on an over-stressed mind and body.

Self-help Measures

Herbal Self-help
For practical purposes, the herbal treatments discussed below will

focus on Western rather than traditional Chinese herbal medicine. This decision has been reached for purely practical reasons, since any item mentioned below should be easily obtainable from a pharmacy or health-food shop, whereas Chinese herbal medicines are not so readily available on an over-the-counter basis. As a result, if the traditional Chinese approach to medicine is attractive to you, it would be appropriate to seek help from a trained practitioner.

It is also worth bearing in mind that several controlled studies have demonstrated that acupuncture has a positive role to play in the treatment of depression. Researchers at the Institute of Acupuncture and Moxibustion in the Academy of Traditional Chinese Medicine at Beijing recently conducted a study which demonstrated that patients who received acupuncture responded as effectively to treatment as a second group who were treated with the antidepressant amitriptyline. After six weeks of treatment and analysis of the data collected, the conclusion was reached that symptoms of anxiety, sleep-disturbance and perceptions of despair were equally reduced in response to acupuncture treatment as to anti-depressant medication. It was also revealed, through an analysis of brain wave patterns, that acupuncture had a perceptively positive effect on the patients' brain waves.

Herbal Help for Anxiety

Soothing herbal teas can provide an excellent alternative to caffeinated teas or coffees. This gives you a double-edged advantage: you will be avoiding regular doses of caffeine, which can contribute to unpleasant sensations of jitteriness and edginess, while also benefiting from the positive, calming, relaxing properties of any of the following herbal teas. Choose from **camomile**, **lime flower** or **valerian** Although valerian is an excellent remedy for easing symptoms of anxiety, agitation, and insomnia, it is best to avoid taking it frequently over an extended period of time. This is because it can paradoxically give rise to symptoms of palpitations or tension headaches when taken in excess. For this reason, always vary the herbal teas that are drunk on a daily basis in order to avoid drinking an excessive amount of a single herb. adding one teaspoonful of dried herb to a cup of hot water. Cover and leave to infuse for 15 minutes before straining and sipping as a calming, soothing beverage.

Anxiety symptoms connected to a general state of nervous exhaustion may benefit from taking diluted tincture of **wild oats** daily. Eight drops of the tincture may be taken in a glass of water, once a day. This may be particularly beneficial if anxiety has arisen as a result of an excess of mental, emotional and physical stress (such as over-working for an extended period of time in order to meet a tight, important deadline).

Underlying problems with tension and anxiety may respond well to one of the proprietary brands of herbal tablets that are on the market. Look for a brand that includes a combination of **hops, valerian and gentian**.

Herbal Help for Depression
A great deal of attention has recently been focused on the therapeutic use of **St John's Wort**. This is due to the way that this herbal medicine appears to have specific advantages when compared to some of the side-effects associated with conventional anti depressants. A report in the *British Medical Journal* drew attention to the fact that German doctors prescribed over 66 million doses of St John's Wort in 1994. In addition, a review of 23 randomized clinical trials of this herbal medicine showed that it was superior to the action of a placebo in treating symptoms of depression. The report in the *BMJ* suggested that St John's Wort may offer advantages in the form of greater safety and tolerability over other conventional drugs used for the same purpose. However, there has also been some controversy over self-help use of St John's Wort, since it has emerged that it can render certain specific conventional drugs inactive when it is prescribed in an unsupervised way. Some herbalists have been outspoken in defending the use of St John's Wort, suggesting that the risks involved should not be over-exaggerated, since responsible use of this herbal medicine should not give rise to huge problems.

The best way to avoid any conflict is to be aware of the types of drugs which may not combine well with St John's Wort. These include any of the following groups of medication: drug treatments for epileptic fits, medicines used to combat rejection of transplant organs, tablets (such as theophylline) used to treat asthma or chronic bronchitis, heart medication such as digoxin, drugs used as anti-clotting agents, the contraceptive pill, drugs used to treat HIV, conventional anti depressants, and medication used to treat migraines.

It is also worth pointing out that, in order to use St John's Wort most safely and effectively, this herbal preparation should be used following a diagnosis of mild to moderate depression by a physician. In other words, this form of herbal medication should not be regarded – as Prozac has been in the past – as a 'happy pill' which can be self-prescribed on a random basis to induce a chemically improved mood, just because we may be feeling a bit low. St John's Wort is most appropriately used where a case of mild to moderate depression has been professionally diagnosed and assessed, and the patient may feel that they want to try an alternative form of treatment rather than conventional anti depressants.

If you are at all unsure or confused about safe guidelines for using St John's Wort, always seek help and advice from your pharmacist, doctor or medical herbalist.

Additional herbal preparations that may also be used in cases of mild to moderate depression include **vervain**, **borage** and **ginseng**.

Aromatherapy Self-help

Although aromatic oils have been used for thousands of years in a healing context, the beneficial effects are becoming increasingly clear in the light of recent research. Studies conducted at Yale University have revealed that certain essential oils can play a part in treating stress-related problems such as high blood pressure. In addition, some essential oils have been revealed to have pain-reducing, mood-balancing and stress-reducing properties.

As yet the precise mechanism by which essential oils affect the body is unclear, but suggestions have been made that aromatic oils may trigger a reaction in the brain which activates the hypothalamus and pituitary glands, in addition to stimulating the limbic system in the brain (the centre for emotion and memory). When used in combination with the relaxing effect of massage, essential oils appear to have an important role to play in relieving accumulated emotional, mental and physical tensions and anxiety.

Aromatherapy Help for Anxiety

Any of the following essential oils may be used, diluted in a carrier oil for a relaxing aromatherapy massage, inhaled from a tissue, added to the bath water for a relaxing soak, or burned in a custom-made vaporizer.

Always remember to dilute essential oils in a carrier oil rather than applying neat oils directly to the skin. For best results add 2 to 3 drops of essential oil to every 5 ml of carrier oil. When bathing, always remember to add 5 or 6 drops of your selected essential oils to the warm bath water after the taps have stopped running so that the oils float on top of the surface.

Appropriate oils to choose from for relief of mild to moderate anxiety include:

- bergamot
- camomile
- clary sage
- lavender
- frankincense
- ylang ylang

Aromatherapy Help for Depression
When aromatherapy is combined with the soothing effect of massage it can have an important role to play in countering the negative effects of stress, and putting you pleasurably back in touch with your body. When you feel low and depressed, the therapeutic effect of essential oils can have a beneficial effect on mood swings, enabling you to feel uplifted, soothed or energized depending on your individual needs at that moment.

Massage itself can also have a significantly positive effect on those who suffer from depression. A study conducted at the university of Miami worked with a group of 52 teenagers hospitalized with symptoms of depression. These were split into two groups for a five-day period, with the first being given a 30-minute massage while the second watched television. It was revealed that the group receiving the massage felt less anxious, were more co-operative, and had measurably lower levels of the stress hormone cortisol than the second group.

Any of the following essential oils may be helpful in easing symptoms of depression – but please note that severe or persistent cases of depression should receive professional treatment rather than self-help measures alone. The following oils may be used diluted with a carrier oil for the purposes of massage, vaporized, or added to a warm, soothing bath for an uplifting, mood-balancing soak:

- camomile
- clary sage
- lavender
- marjoram
- ylang ylang

Homoeopathic Self-help

Homoeopathic remedies can provide an invaluable source of practical help if you suffer from occasional bouts of mild to moderate anxiety. This is especially the case if you want to have access to a type of medical support that bypasses the worrying side-effects of conventional drugs such as tranquillizers.

Provided they are accurately prescribed, homoeopathic remedies provide fast-acting, effective, gentle medicines which are non-habit forming and non-addictive. In fact, it is positively counter-productive to continue taking a homoeopathic remedy once it has done its work.

The most important thing to remember when selecting a homoeopathic remedy for self-help purposes is that it must fit the symptoms of the patient as closely as possible in order to have the maximum beneficial effect. Provided this close match exists, relief of symptoms should rapidly follow.

Homoeopathic remedies can often be successfully prescribed for anticipatory anxiety which descends in response to a coming stressful event. Alternatively, any other episode of mild anxiety that has arisen in response to a specific, unsettling trigger may do very well with homoeopathic self-help. However, well-established, severe cases of anxiety, especially where prescription drugs are being taken on a daily basis, should ideally receive professional treatment from a trained practitioner to assure the most successful outcome.

Homoeopathic Help for Anxiety
Any of the following may be helpful in giving effective, short-term relief of anxiety symptoms. Always bear in mind that only one remedy should be given at any time. If none of the following provides a close enough match to your symptoms, it may be necessary to invest in a more comprehensive self-help guide which, ideally, focuses on the subject of homoeopathic self-help for mental and emotional problems. Alternatively, help and advice may be sought from a homoeopathic practitioner.

Anxiety symptoms which descend rapidly and abruptly with a sense of panic may respond well to **Aconite**. Actual panic attacks may occur, with a powerful feeling that death is near. Problems with anxiety that develop after a shock, such as receiving bad news or being in an accident, may do especially well with this remedy.

Anticipatory anxiety accompanied with a sense of being withdrawn and exhausted may be eased considerably by **Gelsemium**. As the source of anticipatory stress gets nearer there may be problems with painless diarrhoea, as well as a sense of overall trembling and jitteriness.

The different kind of anticipatory anxiety, which results in an unnatural form of extroversion and agitated talkativeness, is likely to do much better with **Arg nit**. Diarrhoea and a generally nervous stomach are also likely to be present, as well as a craving for sweet foods and drinks which make overall symptoms worse.

Anxiety that descends (or is much more severe) at night, accompanied by an overwhelming sense of chilliness and restlessness, may do well with **Arsenicum album**. When this remedy is needed, symptoms are markedly worse when you are alone (which is why the night can be a focus of anxiety), and are soothed by distractions and being in warm, cosy surroundings.

Jitteriness and anxiety specifically related to stressful situations where there is a tendency to rely on stimulants such as coffee to keep going, and cigarettes and alcohol to wind down, may respond well to **Nux vomica**. This type of anxiety characteristically takes the form of being on a 'short fuse' with lots of anxious irritability, insomnia and tension headaches.

'Free-floating' anxiety with extreme sensitivity to the feelings of others may do well with **Phosphorus**. Those who respond well to this remedy tend to be outgoing, sociable and given to all sorts of enthusiasms, with a corresponding tendency to become quickly drained, exhausted and apathetic. Reassurance and comfort reduce levels of this anxiety, while an excess of stimulation can make things worse.

Homoeopathic Help for Depression
Homoeopathic remedies can be extremely effective in acting as mood-balancing agents, while at the same time stimulating improved energy levels and renewing a basic sense of well-being.

This is due to the way that an appropriately selected homoeopathic prescription appears to act as a catalyst, giving the whole system the needed boost to reach a state of mental, emotional and physical equilibrium. Since this is a rather ambitious undertaking, anyone seeking help for problems with well-established depression should seek help from a trained practitioner rather than trying to prescribe for themselves. This avoids the complication of having to be unrealistically objective about your feelings and moods when you are feeling low (this objectivity is not a problem for a trained practitioner to achieve, since they are outside the situation).

Secondly, if conventional drugs are already being taken as a treatment for depression, seeking responsible professional help can keep you from experimenting with reducing your conventional anti depressants prematurely, too quickly, or ill-advisably.

On the other hand, mild phases of depression which appear in response to a known trigger (for instance, occasional pre-menstrual blues) may respond well to homoeopathic self-help, in addition to positive lifestyle changes such as those discussed in Chapter Eight.

If symptoms do not continue to improve, or if it becomes necessary to rely almost permanently on homoeopathic support to maintain a reasonable sense of emotional equilibrium, it is time to seek help and advice from a trained practitioner.

Depressive feelings that are combined with a sense of being exhausted and stressed to the limit, with a resulting lowered libido and indifference towards any expression of sexual interest, may respond to **Sepia**. When this remedy is indicated there is a general sense of cheering up and feeling more positive in response to aerobic exercise.

A depressed mood which descends pre-menstrually and resolves itself as soon as a period begins may be greatly improved by **Lachesis**. When this homoeopathic remedy is needed, mood swings are very abrupt and marked, with chattiness and sociability alternating with a sense of withdrawal and a need for solitude. Because all symptoms tend to be worse after a sleep, there may be an aversion to going to bed when feeling emotionally low.

Weepy depression with a significant relief of symptoms after a good cry in sympathetic company may do well with **Pulsatilla**. Symptoms calling for this remedy include feeling depressed and despondent, with a tendency to burst into tears at the least provocation. Mood swings may respond well to taking gentle exercise in the fresh air, while being indoors alone may make a low mood more severe.

A form of withdrawn depression with a resulting strong aversion to company may do well in response to **Nat mur**. When this remedy is indicated, depression often occurs as a delayed reaction to unexpressed grief or long-term emotional strain. There may be a strong dislike of being in sympathetic company because of a genuine dislike of bursting into tears in public. This is seen as a humiliating experience and, as a result, is avoided at all costs.

If depression has descended following exposure to an excessive amount of stress at work, with a tendency to feel anxious and despondent about reaching fastidiously high standards, it is worth considering the remedy **Arsenicum album**. When this is indicated, symptoms of depression occur in combination with anxiety which is most severe at night. Someone who benefits from this remedy becomes fussy, fidgety, obsessive and extremely self-critical, as well as being intolerant of mistakes made by others.

SAM-e: The Wonder Supplement?
Although the supplement SAM-e is not a herbal or homoeopathic medicine, aromatherapy product or nutritional supplement, it is important to include it within this chapter, since it is gaining a reputation as being at least as effective as St John's Wort as an alternative way of combating depression.

A great deal of research has been conducted into the efficacy and safety of SAM-e, and results of clinical studies so far reveal that it appears to be as effective as conventional antidepressants in treating mild to moderate depression, while appearing to avoid causing any serious side-effects. In several clinical trials, SAM-e has been shown to give rise to fewer side-effects than a placebo (unmedicated sugar pill). At extremely high doses (far in excess of the recommended dose) it may cause some digestive symptoms such as heartburn or diarrhoea. In addition, in very high doses it may also give rise to headaches.

SAM-e is a compound that is naturally produced in our bodies through a process called methylation, and appears to be implicated in a wide range of basic bodily functions and processes. Not only does supplementation with SAM-e appear to relieve symptoms of moderate depression, but it also appears to have a beneficial effect on the pain of arthritis and fibromyalgia.

One of the most impressive aspects of SAM-e's action is the way in which it appears to take half the time of conventional antidepressants to show positive results. Studies have revealed that the beneficial effects can be apparent within a week of taking SAM-e, in contrast to conventional antidepressants which can take anything from two to six weeks before the patient begins to see a perceptible improvement.

In order to achieve maximum absorption and efficacy, it has been suggested that SAM-e should ideally be taken on an empty stomach approximately half an hour before meals. The recommended dosage can vary between 400 and 800 milligrams per day. If 400 mg or less are taken each day, this may be achieved by taking the whole dose at once. Those who take 600 to 800 mg each day should take SAM-e in two divided doses, with each one being taken on an empty stomach. The general recommended starting dose is 400 mg a day. If this dose is not effective within two weeks of use, it may be increased to 800 mg a day.

As yet there have been no reports of any adverse interaction between SAM-e and any other prescription drugs, herbal medicines or vitamin supplements. However, it has been suggested that it is wise not to combine SAM-e with antidepressants such as MAOIs. In cases of severe or manic depression, SAM-e should only be used with strict psychiatric supervision, since there is a possibility that manic episodes may become more volatile.

Although there are no reported negative effects of taking SAM-e in conjunction with conventional antidepressants, at the moment it is best to err on the side of caution and only embark on a course of taking SAM-e with the full knowledge and support of your psychiatrist or doctor. If they are unaware of the existence and clinical track record of SAM-e, there is an abundance of published information available, so they can assess for themselves how suitable it may be for be use in your individual case. It is also worth pointing out that long-term treatment with SAM-e can be an expensive undertaking.

How and Where to Obtain Good Quality Alternative Medicines

The days have gone when finding a decent range of homoeopathic and herbal medicines involved a trek to the nearest specialist health food shop. Today you should be able to find most of the items mentioned in the above sections in your local high-street pharmacy, where you will find a significant portion of their shelf-space devoted to alternative and complementary products, including homoeopathic and herbal medicines and a decent range of essential oils and nutritional supplements.

If you are looking for something that cannot easily be found in your local pharmacy, a well-stocked health-food shop is likely to be your next best option. Alternatively, many specialist outlets such as homoeopathic pharmacies and manufacturers of essential oils provide a mail order service. See the Useful Addresses section for the names and addresses of reputable suppliers of herbal, homoeopathic and essential oils products.

Chapter Eight

Lifestyle Changes

If you are concerned about giving yourself the maximum chance of recovering well from anxiety and depression, there are specific lifestyle factors that you really do need to take on board. These positive improvements in your pattern of living make a genuine difference to your state of mind, as well as your general state of health. Perhaps most significantly, by taking charge of less-than-healthy aspects of your lifestyle you are likely to find that you experience fewer of the unpleasant, powerless sensations which many people feel in the face of the distress of anxiety and depression. Discovering that there are practical steps which can play an important role in hastening your recovery can be immensely liberating.

The most difficult part is finding the initial motivation, since many people suffering from depression find that they may feel that there is little point in doing anything because they feel so negative. In addition, those who have problems with anxiety may feel threatened and alarmed at trying anything new. However, if you can take the first steps to integrate relaxation, meditation, improved nutrition and regular exercise into your life, the hardest part is over. Once these positive lifestyle changes become established, you are unlikely to want to give up the positive benefits that you have begun to experience. This, in turn, gives you the extra motivation to keep going.

Always remember that the key to success is making sure that you don't take on too much too soon. By being unrealistically ambitious you can unwittingly sabotage your own efforts. This is notoriously the case with unrealistic eating patterns or exercise plans – many of us start out with great intentions, but find to our dismay that we just can't keep the pace. This is only going to lead to reinforced feelings of guilt and failure, which anyone with a tendency to be depressed will have an abundance of in the first place. Instead, make a point of restricting yourself to a commitment of time that you know you can spare without undue effort. This way you should find that your positive changes dovetail seamlessly into your life so that they should begin to feel a natural part of day-to-day living.

Relaxation

Engaging in a regular relaxation exercise can be one of the most effective tools in combating feelings of anxiety and mental, emotional and physical tension. By making regular relaxation a part of your life you are giving your mind and body a chance to unwind: something that just isn't possible sitting in front of the television at the end of the day with a drink and a cigarette. Unlike the effects of a guided relaxation exercise, the knock-on effects of alcohol and nicotine are likely to make you feel slightly depressed, while the stimulation of a television programme late at night can lead to a less-than-satisfying sleep pattern.

The simple relaxation exercise given in the section below can be an invaluable tool you can use whenever you feel tense and anxious. Once you become familiar with the sensations involved, you can make use of the breathing technique whenever you feel under pressure or on edge. Apart from the practical advantages to be found in having a simple relaxation exercise you can call on whenever you need to calm down, there are longer-term advantages of making use of a regular relaxation technique. These include improved concentration, less fatigue (as a result of fewer episodes of agitation and panic), improved sleep quality and fewer muscle aches and tension headaches.

A Guided Relaxation Exercise
When learning how to relax, it is very important to ensure that your surroundings are as conducive to a relaxed, peaceful state as possible. The room which you are going to use should be comfortably warm and quiet. It's helpful to choose somewhere where the phone is unlikely to disturb you. Persistent background noise of any kind does not encourage deep relaxation. Whatever you wear should feel extremely comfortable, non-restrictive and warm always remember that there is a tendency for body temperature to drop during deep relaxation. You don't want to find you are being distracted by suddenly feeling uncomfortably chilly.

When doing the following relaxation exercise, it is best to begin lying on your back on the floor, since this will give you the best chance of feeling the different sensations as your breathing pattern changes and your muscles relax. However, as you become more proficient and aware of how to achieve a state of mental and physical relaxation, you may choose to practise your relaxation technique in a straight-backed chair with your feet resting comfortably on the floor, or sitting cross-legged on the floor. Always remember, the most important thing is that you should choose whatever feels most comfortable for you if you are to truly experience a deep sense of relaxation.

Once you are in a comfortable position, rest one hand on your abdomen at the level of your navel. Don't change your breathing pattern in any way at the moment, just observe the way in which you are breathing (for instance, how deeply and how fast). There is a very good chance that you will find that your hand is hardly moving at all, since most people use only the upper part of their chest when they breathe. Since this is often coupled with a tendency to breathe quite rapidly when stressed, by adopting this pattern of breathing you are unwittingly making yourself feel more tense and anxious. This is due to the chemical imbalance that occurs between carbon dioxide and oxygen in your system. This can, however, be swiftly and effectively rectified by learning how to breathe using your whole lung capacity. This involves something called *diaphragmatic breathing*, and this is what we will be concentrating on achieving in this relaxation exercise.

- Inhale slowly and steadily until you find that the hand resting on your belly lifts upwards as your lungs fill with air. As you exhale, your hand should sink back to its original position as your lungs empty from the base to the top. Never force the depth or the pace of your breathing: what you should ideally be aiming for is a smooth, gentle expansion and deflation of your lungs with each inhalation and exhalation. If at any point you feel dizzy or light-headed, just return to a normal breathing pattern for a few breaths before beginning diaphragmatic breathing once again.
- As a steady rhythm of diaphragmatic breathing is established, you should find that you feel calmer, more relaxed and less tense. If you are lying on your back, feel your legs relax against the surface of the floor, letting your feet fall apart slightly as you let go of them.

Your arms should also relax against the surface you are lying on, with the backs of your hands making gentle contact with the floor.

- It's now time to bring your attention to your head and face. Beginning at the crown of your head, imagine that you are letting go of any tension in the muscles of your scalp. Mentally move in this way down your hairline and forehead, letting go of any tension that you sense on your way. Do the same with the muscles of your face, concentrating especially closely on common areas where tension may be held such as the muscles surrounding the joint of the jaw and the mouth. You may find that, as your face relaxes, your lips part gently – this is a positive indication that your face is becoming more relaxed.

- Continue this process as you move down each area of your body, from your neck and shoulders to your chest, back, buttocks, abdomen, thighs, calves, ankles and feet. If you find any areas that feel especially tense and tight, spend some extra time consciously relaxing these until they feel looser and less tense.

- Finish this exercise very slowly. Gradually bring your attention back to your surroundings. Move your fingers and toes gently, stretching and flexing them in turn. Slowly stretch and flex the large muscles in your arms and legs until you are ready to stretch your whole body. Now is a good time to compare how your whole body feels compared with how you felt before the relaxation exercise began.

- Slowly open your eyes, making sure that you don't sit up too abruptly. Instead, roll gently on to one side and move slowly into a sitting position.

Once you have completed this exercise you should feel extremely comfortable and thoroughly relaxed. Now bring your attention back to your pattern of breathing you should discover that it has naturally slowed down and regulated itself to a smooth, comfortable pattern.

How to Meditate

The regular practice of meditation appears to have a significant effect in assisting in releasing tension as well as elevating mood. A fascinating study conducted at the School of Behavioural Sciences in North

Queensland, Australia revealed that meditation has an observable and quantifiable effect on our moods and hormone levels, similar to the responses that occur in the bodies of long-distance runners. The conclusion reached as a result of this study was that both vigorous aerobic activity (such as running) and meditation appear to have a positive influence on the participants' moods. This is thought to be connected to fluctuations in blood plasma levels of corticotrophin-releasing hormone, which is influenced by both types of activity.

Additional benefits of the regular practice of meditation include greater clarity of thought, improved decision-making ability, and improved memory.

A Simple Meditation Exercise
Prepare for meditation in the same way as you prepared for the relaxation exercise. The surroundings should be comfortably warm and quiet, and as free from any distractions or intrusions as possible.

Meditation should ideally be done sitting as comfortably as possible, with your spine balanced and straight. Whether you sit in a straight-backed chair or cross-legged on a cushion on the floor is really a matter of personal choice and preference. Your main priority should be to achieve as comfortable a position as possible so that you avoid being distracted by discomfort of any kind.

● Consciously try to empty your mind of any distracting or disturbing thoughts by focusing on an object or image. This could be something that is sitting in front of you (such as a lighted candle or a flower), or you may choose to concentrate on a mental image that is compelling, uplifting or soothing to you. Alternatively, try shutting your eyes and repeating a sound to yourself regularly over and over again. This need not be anything more complicated than repeating the word 'one' to yourself as you breathe in and out.

It is almost inevitable that distracting thoughts will wander into your mind when you first attempt to meditate. Don't be worried by this, just mentally put them to one side and focus once again on your selected image or sound. Strange as it may sound, this does genuinely get easier with time and repeated practice.

You may find that one of the hardest things to do when you are feeling low and depressed is to stop sabotaging yourself with negative assumptions. When this tendency is combined with an underlying feeling of anxiety, the scene is unfortunately set for you to start 'catastrophizing', which has the unpleasant knock-on effect of making you feel even more tense and depressed. When you 'catastrophize' you tend to react to what is often in reality only a minor set-back as if it were a major problem that is going to lead to major negative consequences. The dreadful thing about this insidious process is that you may find that you can envisage the awful consequences in grisly detail, as you picture the major crisis looming ahead. With this sort of mind-set at work you are unlikely to be able to see whatever situation you are in from a balanced, realistic perspective. The good news, however, is that once you get to grips with your problems with anxiety and depression, as a result of benefiting from effective treatment and self-help measures, you will find that you naturally tend to catastrophize less and less.

Another major weapon you have at your disposal in dealing with self-sabotage is the pursuit of consciously building up your reserves of self-esteem. You shouldn't be put off by feeling that spending time nurturing yourself is somehow unacceptably self-indulgent. Look on the following advice, instead, as a maintenance programme that will help you roll more effectively and resiliently with the punches that life inevitably throws at you from time to time. By developing greater mental and emotional balance you are likely to save yourself an enormous amount of time and psychological trauma further down the line.

Simple Self-esteem Boosters
● Try to build some time for yourself into every day. This need be no more than 15 minutes if time is in very short supply, but however long it is, this interval of time needs to be spent doing something that is enjoyable. This can vary enormously from person to person, depending on your personal preferences, moods and interests. Some people may want to listen to music, take a walk, meditate, chat with a close friend, read a novel, watch a favourite

video, have a bath with added essential oils or do some yoga. Choose whatever suits you, but make sure that whatever you do recharges your emotional batteries in some way. Above all, defend this personal time, making sure that others don't make you feel guilty about looking after yourself.

- Avoid, or limit your exposure to, people you know make you feel negative or emotionally drained. Excessively needy people can be extremely unaware of when they are psychologically exhausting someone else, because they are so focused on and preoccupied with their own problems.

- Make sure that you spend as much time as possible with those who make you feel optimistic and positive: this can be an excellent way of topping up your self-esteem batteries. Although when you feel low you may have a tendency to avoid company, it can be helpful to try to get yourself in sympathetic company.

- When something minor goes wrong, try to see it as a temporary set-back rather than a sign of failure on your part. If anything useful can be learned from it, try to take it on board in as unself-critical away as possible, then move on. By doing so, you will be able to nip a vicious circle of catastrophies in the bud. As a result you save yourself a lot of trauma and emotional exhaustion.

- If you begin to see the familiar signs of depression surfacing, try to remind yourself that this has happened before, and your mood has re-balanced itself eventually. If you find you can't hold on to this thought, get a close friend or relative to gently remind you of your recovery in the past. If panic attacks are a problem it can also be of great help and comfort to keep reassuring yourself that no one has ever died or suffered any lasting, severe consequences of experiencing a panic attack.

- Above all else, always try to avoid the trap of feeling guilty or to blame about feeling depressed. Depression is a particularly cruel condition, since many people who have never experienced clinical depression fail to understand that it is an illness beyond someone's conscious control. As a result, one of the least helpful things to say to a depressive is 'just pull yourself together', regardless of how kindly it may be meant. If you are struggling with depression, try instead to see yourself as a basically good person who is trying to cope to the best of your ability with the symptoms of an illness.

Different forms of physical activity can be immensely beneficial if you suffer from anxiety and depression. Feelings of anxiety and jitteriness which arise as a result of exposure to ongoing stress can be greatly helped by regular exercise. Vigorous, aerobic activity that gives your heart and lungs a regular work out can do a great deal to dispel – the symptoms of feeling emotionally 'on edge' which arise from an excess of adrenaline circulating in your system. Since the 'fight or flight' response is triggered when you are under emotional stress, regular, aerobic exercise such as cycling, swimming or 'power' walking gives you an invaluable outlet for burning off any excess adrenaline.

In addition, it has been revealed that regular, enjoyable aerobic exercise has a powerful antidepressant effect. This appears to be linked to the way in which vigorous, rhythmical exercise stimulates the production of chemicals called endorphins in the body. These naturally produced, pleasure-giving, pain-relieving chemicals are responsible for the emotional 'high' that many experience after exercising. In addition, the chances are that if you engage in regular, aerobic exercise you are also likely to feel an increased sense of self-esteem and self-confidence, which comes from knowing that your body is stronger, fitter and sleeker.

Don't be put off by thinking you have to take out an expensive subscription to a gym and wear the latest lycra fitness clothes in order to reap the benefits of aerobic exercise. All you need to do is take up a regular walking routine each day and stick to it. The only specialized equipment needed is a comfortable pair of trainers that give your feet the necessary support and comfort. The rest is down to you.

It is best to aim for a walk that lasts at least half an hour, but if the idea is initially off-putting because you feel unfit and unmotivated, start with a five- or ten-minute walk at first. Once you establish a routine, you can expand the time spent on the walk, going a little further each time. Remember to walk at a brisk pace rather than an amble, but not so fast that breathlessness becomes a problem. If you are working at a desirable aerobic level, you should find that you can continue a conversation without strain or feeling short of breath.

It can also be helpful to remember that the times when you may feel the least motivated are likely to be the very times when you need the benefits of aerobic activity most. So, if you can muster up the 'get up and go' when you feel down in the dumps, muzzy-headed or sleepy, you are likely to feel clearer-headed, more energized and less sluggish after a walk.

Other possibilities for supplementing aerobic exercise include cycling (either in the open air or using a stationary exercise bike at home) or swimming.

The regular practice of yoga also appears to play an important role in helping those who suffer from depression and anxiety. This appears to be connected to the emphasis in yoga on the importance of breathing consciously from the diaphragm while executing the postures. As a result, you may find that the regular practice of yoga induces a more relaxed state of mind, and encourages a greater sense of harmony between mind, emotions and body. There are also additional benefits in the form of greater flexibility, stamina and boosted energy levels.

Yoga is also likely to appeal to those put off by any approach to exercise that is overly competitive, frenetic, spartan or punishing. When you practise yoga you are in competition with no one else, and you are certainly discouraged from any pursuit that resembles the 'no pain, no gain' or 'going for the burn' preoccupations of the 1980s. In fact, if you experience any pain while executing a yoga posture this is interpreted as a negative sign that you are pushing your body beyond an acceptable limit and that you need to stop.

Yoga also appears to have tangible benefits for those who are stressed and anxious. There is a formidable amount of evidence that suggests that regular, advanced practice of yoga enables you to gain an impressive amount of control over organs that are usually regarded as involuntary in their function. These organs include the heart, lungs, and those that make up the nervous system. Practitioners of yoga who have been observed in clinical studies have shown their capacity to consciously and dramatically slow down their respiration and heart rate for an extended period of time. Those who suffer from high blood pressure and circulatory problems have been shown to benefit from responsibly taught yoga.

Basic Advice on Getting Moving

If you have not exercised for a very long time, and feel rather intimidated by the idea of making regular physical activity part of your life, the following advice may be helpful.

- Always avoid the temptation to go for too radical a programme at first. Being over-ambitious at the outset, then not being able to meet the commitment, is one of the most common reasons why many of us give up a fitness programme.
- Keep it short and keep it simple at the beginning. Although it may sound ridiculously unambitious at first, it is best to aim for five or ten minutes of aerobic activity a day. This is far easier to commit to than a goal of 40 minutes from the very first day, which you probably can't spare and won't stick to.
- If you don't have the time to enrol in a yoga class, try learning the postures at home with the help of a video aimed at teaching yoga to beginners. Advice on the best tapes available may be gained from any friends who are yoga enthusiasts, or getting in touch with the Wheel of Yoga. The latter should also be able to put you in touch with qualified teachers in your area.
- Always make sure that whatever fitness activity you choose fits in with your temperament and interests. Enjoyment is one of the most essential factors in ensuring that you'll stick to whatever fitness programme you have chosen. If you are bored you are bound to give up very quickly.
- Try to include a range of different activities in your fitness schedule in order to guard against boredom setting in, and to make sure that you get an all-round body-conditioning programme. Possibilities include walking, swimming, cycling, weight-training, yoga, t'ai chi, Pilates, tennis, badminton, kick boxing, and tone-and-stretch classes.

Chapter Nine

Advice for Carers

Any book of practical advice on anxiety and depression is not complete if it does not consider the perspective of those who share a close relationship with the person who is suffering. Whether we are the lover, mother, father, brother, sister, close colleague or friend of a severely anxious and depressed person, we are likely to find the experience physically and emotionally draining, trying, distressing, maddening and downright exhausting at times. This is obviously more intense for those who live in close proximity with the person who is ill, rather than those who have frequent but less day-to-day contact. On the other hand, the sense of delight, sheer relief and pleasure that comes from watching the definite signs of recovery take place can more than compensate for the negative experiences of supporting someone who is severely depressed.

However, if we are being realistic it would be a serious mistake not to admit that living with a clinically anxious and depressed relative can put a serious strain on any relationship, sometimes to the point of threatening to destroy it. As a result of this immense psychological strain, it is vitally important to consider practical ways of caring for the carer, so that they don't get drained and psychologically dragged down as well.

The following simple advice will give you some idea of the strategies that can be employed in order to maximize any carer's ability to come through this extremely emotionally challenging experience not just intact, but possibly stronger, and in possession of more self-knowledge and awareness than before the crisis descended.

How to Support Someone Suffering from Anxiety and Depression

Sadly, one of the most confusing things about being depressed is that, although it is very common to feel anxiety about feeling isolated, an awful lot of features of a depressed person's behaviour are not designed to attract company. In fact, although being alone is something that is not consciously desired when we are depressed, the sad reality is that we may end up acting in such a way that lovers, relatives and friends keep their emotional and physical distance from us. Once you understand this basic dilemma, it may make it possible for us to see that a depressed person may be crying out for company and attention, even when they are behaving in what is an apparently anti-social way. In such a situation, it can be helpful not to have a knee-jerk reaction to the alienating behaviour, but to try to stand back for a moment and try to communicate at a deeper level with the person who is depressed by showing as much warmth and understanding as you can. It is common for those who are depressed to feel deeply unlovable and unloved: if you can respond in a genuinely compassionate and non-judgemental way it provides the depressed person with an opportunity to respond in a positive way.

However much you might feel tempted to do so, never tell a depressed person to 'just pull yourself together and snap out of it.' Depression and anxiety are real illnesses, just like diabetes or multiple sclerosis, and of course it would be unthinkable to tell a victim of either of the latter two conditions to just snap out of their problems. Mental and emotional disorders are particularly cruel forms of illness due to the absence of physical signs and symptoms. Plenty of people will get a great deal of sympathy and attention if they have broken an arm or a leg, because the problem is so obvious and visible. The pain and suffering of anxiety and depression are no less real because we cannot see them, in fact they can be greater because we can forget they are there, and not make any allowances for them as a result.

If, after reading this book, you feel a close relative may be suffering from undiagnosed anxiety and depression, make sure that they see their doctor in order to ask for help. This can be a particular problem for men, who may feel instinctively uncomfortable about asking for help and advice if they feel anxious or depressed, since they may feel that this is partly an admission of weakness. This male fear of vulnerability is thought to be part of the reason why far more women than men are diagnosed as suffering from depression, since women on the whole are thought to be more comfortable with acknowledging problems of a non-physical nature. Since there are so many avenues of support open to anyone suffering from anxiety or depression, it is very sad if these positive opportunities for treatment are missed due to avoiding asking for appropriate help when necessary. If someone is in too passive a state to go out and see their doctor, arrange for the doctor to come and see them. This may be especially appropriate if the person who is depressed is elderly or suffering from limited mobility.

If the person who is depressed is living alone, keep in touch regularly by a combination of telephone calls and visits. Preparing the occasional meal or giving help with household chores can be a lifesaver to someone who is going through an especially down phase, since at times like these it can take what seems a superhuman effort to accomplish even the most basic of tasks.

Make sure, as far as possible, that the depressed person takes frequent exercise. This need be nothing more ambitious than taking a regular walk each day, or having a swim at a nearby pool. Since it is natural for someone who is depressed to become very introspective and disinclined to take the initiative to go out, even when it may be very necessary, suggest going out for a coffee, a brief shopping trip, or for a drive into the country for a change of scene.

Try to counter negative statements with appropriate positive perspectives. Although this may not always be appreciated or appropriate, in certain situations it can be extremely important to balance an unrealistically bleak perspective with a more rational one. Avoid the temptation to overdo it (such as saying 'everything will be fine' in the face of a situation where this is obviously not the case), since this will only make the depressed person more agitated, angry and desperate. On the other hand, if something is being said that is unrealistically negative, and basically untrue, it is important to correct this biased reflection with a positive description of the truth. So if someone who is depressed comes out with a comment such as 'I am totally unlikable and worthless', remind them of all of the people who care for them, including yourself.

Check that you may not be unwittingly encouraging someone to remain in a passive, depressed state. In some situations, caring for someone who is depressed can put us in a position of strength because someone is dependent upon us, and may give us a significant feeling of playing an important role. When this happens we may unwittingly collude with someone else's illness. Ask yourself how you feel when you picture the depressed person who is close to you recovering fully and returning to their previous independent existence. If your gut instinct is to feel threatened, the chances are that there are some issues that need to be explored around the question of dependency.

Who Cares for the Carer?

Here are some simple techniques for self-nurturing and self-support, for anyone caring for someone who is emotionally vulnerable and needy.

Anyone who is involved in supporting an anxious and depressed person back to health is likely to be so immersed in problem-solving for that person that they instinctively forget about themselves. While this may do no harm in the short term, if you ignore your own emotional and physical needs for too long it can have an extremely destructive effect, leaving you emotionally, mentally and physically exhausted.

This need not happen if you make sure you work within specific, practical boundaries. It makes a great deal of sense to make sure that you guard against depleting your energy reserves unnecessarily, and look after yourself properly. Following the practical advice that follows should help you to remain sufficiently resilient to carry on caring for the depressed and anxious person who is close to you, as well as yourself.

Above all, fight the instinct to feel guilty if you feel you have given enough of yourself for the moment and need a temporary respite in order to re-charge your batteries. If suggestions are being made – overtly or subtly – about your being selfish in meeting your own needs, it can be helpful to point out that if you become exhausted and burnt out it isn't going to be in anybody's interest, least of all that of the depressed person.

Since anyone who is depressed or anxious can be very needy and require a great deal of time and attention, make sure that you have plenty of time available to spend in company that you find positive and uplifting. In this way your own mental and emotional batteries are less at risk of becoming flat and empty. It is also a very important way of ensuring that you retain a healthy balance in your own life. This is particularly important, since a depressed or anxious person can have an acute sense that normal life has ceased to exist. By keeping in touch with the day-to-day experience of life outside the depressed person's home, you may be able to bring some of the atmosphere of normality with you when you spend time with them.

Draw on as much professional support as possible in helping the depressed person with their problems. It can be very dangerous and personally destructive if you start to believe that it is up to you to provide the necessary support to solve the depressed and anxious person's problems. Answers to these problems are far more likely to be found in a combination of appropriate professional support, exploration of self-help measures, resolution of external problems and the passage of time. Provide all of the extra support, love, understanding and patience that you can, but always resist becoming a martyr by shouldering an unrealistic amount of responsibility.

Make use of self-help measures that are restorative, calming, and energizing in turn. These could consist of any combination of self-help support recommended in this book, depending on your particular temperament and inclination.

Regular exercise such as running, cycling or swimming can be an invaluable ally in channelling excess adrenaline when we feel stressed to the limit and wound-up. Alternatively, regular practice of yoga can be a tremendous source of relaxation and a promoter of optimum emotional balance and equilibrium.

Be conscious of the potential power that the depressed person can exert. When someone is weak and dependent it can be easy to be unwittingly manipulated into colluding with the situation. As a result, you may find yourself becoming involved in doing things for the depressed person, to a point that encourages them to become even more passive and incapacitated. This is not inevitably the case, since there will be situations that arise involving genuine, desperate need. If you suspect you are moving into a situation that is potentially one of unhealthy collusion, it will be helpful to talk your concerns over with someone who is not emotionally involved in the situation. They will be able to adopt a more objective stance which will allow them to evaluate the reality of the situation more effectively. This perspective could be provided by a counsellor, social worker or doctor.

Make it a priority never to lose touch with your sense of humour.

Spend time with friends who are light-hearted, and watch videos of favourite comic films whenever you feel at risk of feeling blue yourself. Always avoid the temptation when feeling low yourself to take refuge in unhelpful ways of escape such as alcohol or cigarettes. While these may give the illusion in the short term of making you feel more relaxed or uplifted, they are likely to give rise to more problems than they solve in the long term.

When to Call on Extra Help

- Any suggestion that the depressed person is contemplating suicide requires professional support and input. Under no circumstances should this responsibility be shouldered alone by whoever is supporting a severely depressed and/or anxious person.
- If signs of anxiety or developing depression emerge in a carer, they must seek help and extra professional support for themselves.
- If meeting the practical and emotional needs of a depressed person is beginning to eat into the day-to-day experience of the carer to the point where he or she can no longer live a normal life, this is a sure sign that more support is needed.
- Although it is extremely important for someone who is anxious or depressed to have the opportunity to express their feelings freely and openly with those who are closest to them, additional, professional support is also likely to be necessary whenever depression continues over an extended period of time, or if it is especially severe in its nature. This is due to the way that those who are close to someone suffering from depression are often too emotionally involved to be able to listen uncritically to the destructive or negative feelings being expressed, no matter how hard they try. It is also true that carers often find their emotional resources are put under such a strain that they become unable to provide the calm, sympathetic listening ear that is needed at especially fraught times. As a result, it can be invaluable to have the opportunity to talk freely about emotional problems with a psychotherapist or counsellor, who will be able to take an objective, non-judgemental stance. Due to this professional distance, it is possible for the therapist to interpret what is being said from a professional perspective, encouraging their client to explore issues which are likely to result in valuable emotional insights.

Useful Addresses

Aromatherapy Organisations Council

PO Box 19834
London SE25 6WF
Tel: and Fax: 020 8251 7912

British Acupuncture Council

Park House
206-208 Latimer Road
London W10 6RE
020 8964 0333
e-mail: info@acupuncture.org.uk

British Association for Counselling

37a Sheep Street
Rugby
Warwicks
CV21 3BJ
01788 550899

British Wheel of Yoga

1 Hamilton Place
Boston Road
Sleaford
Lincs NG34 7ES
01529 306 851
Tel: and Fax: 01529 303233

Depressives Anonymous

36 Chestnut Avenue
Beverley, Humberside HU17 9QU
01482 887634

MIND/National Association for Mental Health

Granta House, 15-19 Broadway
London E15 4BQ
020 8519 2122/020 8522 1728
MIND information line (operates 9.15 – 4.45 Monday,
Wednesday, Thursday, Friday and 2 – 4.45 on Tuesday)
www.mind.org.uk

No Panic

93 Brandsfarm Way
Randlay
Telford, Shrops TF3 2JQ
01952 590005 (office number)
01952 590545 (helpline)

National Institute of Medical Herbalists

56 Longbrooke Street
Exeter, Devon EX4 8HA
01392 420622

The Nutri Centre

The Hale Clinic
7 Park Crescent
London W1N 3HE
020 74365122

Society for the Promotion of Nutritional Therapy

BCM Box SPNT
London
WC1N 3XX
01825 872921

Relate (Couple Counselling)

Herbert Gray College
Little Church Street
Rugby
Warwicks CV21 3AP
01788 565675

SAD Association

PO Box 989
London SW7 2PZ
01903 814942

The Samaritans

10 The Grove
Slough
Berks SL1 1QP
National helpline: 0845 909090
www.samaritans.org.uk

The Society of Homoeopaths

2 Artizan Road
Northampton NN1 4HU
01604 621400
www.nhsconfed.net/bha

Tai Chi

Tai Chi Union of Great Britain
94 Felsham Road
London SW15 1DQ
020 8780 1063
e-mail: comptonph@aol.com

Transcendental Meditation

Freepost
London SW1P 4YY
0990 143733

Triumph Over Phobia

PO Box 1831
Bath BA1 3XY
e-mail: clientsoverphobia@compuserve.com

United Kingdom Council for Psychotherapy

Regent's College
Regent's Park
London NW1 4NS
020 7436 3002
www.psychotherapy.org.uk

Recommended Reading

Brown, Richard MD, Bottiglieri, Terry, and Colman, Carol, *Stop Depression Now: SAM-e the Amazing New Treatment for Depression, Joint Pain, Fibromyalgia, and Other Conditions* (Berkeley Books, 2000)

Downing-Orr, Dr Kristina, *What to Do If You're Burned Out and Blue: The Essential Guide to Help You Through Depression* (Thorsons, 2000)

Dryden, Professor Windy, and Feltham, Colin, *Counselling and Psychotherapy: A Consumer's Guide* (Sheldon Press, 1995)

Gillett, Dr Richard, *Overcoming Depression: A Practical Self-Help Guide to Prevention and Treatment* (Dorling Kindersley, 1987)

Ingham, Christine, *Panic Attacks: What They Are, Why They Happen, and What You Can Do About Them* (Thorsons, 1993)

MacEoin, Beth, *Natural Medicine: A Practical Guide to Family Health* (Bloomsbury, 2000)

Rowe, Dorothy, *Depression: The Way Out of Your Prison* (Routledge and Kegan Paul, 1996)

Sachs, Judith, *Nature's Prozac, Natural Ways to Achieve Peak Mental and Emotional Health* (Simon and Schuster Ltd, 1997)

Trickett, Shirley, *Coping with Anxiety and Depression* (Sheldon Press, 1989)

Weekes, Dr Claire, *Essential Help for Your Nerves: Recover from Nervous Fatigue and Overcome Stress and Fear* (Thorsons, 2000)

Glossary

Adrenaline:
One of the principal blood -ressure-raising hormones used medicinally as a heart stimulant, and as a muscle relaxant in bronchial asthma.

Anthroposophical medicine:
A holistic form of treatment developed by the Austrian scientist Rudolf Steiner which aims to treat the whole person and not just the symptoms of illness.

Anti-oxidant nutrients:
Nutrients that assist the body in dealing with the negative effects of oxidation in the body. These effects include an increased tendency to develop degenerative diseases and signs of premature ageing.

Aromatherapy:
The use of essential oils in order to stimulate the healing process. Oils may be diluted and massaged on to the skin, added to bath water, or vaporized in a specially-designed oil burner.

Ayurvedic medicine:
A holistic system of healing that has been practised for generations in India and neighbouring countries.

Behaviour therapy:
A psychological approach which is aimed at helping the client face situations that are the focus of anxiety and distress.

Beta-blockers:
Drugs that are prescribed to relieve the symptoms of high blood pressure and anxiety attacks. They work by regulating the rhythm of the heart.

Chinese herbal medicine:	An important component of traditional Chinese medicine which involves the prescription of Chinese herbs. Chinese herbal medicine has recently gained a great deal of publicity due to its potential for relieving chronic skin conditions such as eczema.
Cognitive therapy:	A psychological approach to anxiety and depression which shows us how to identify and break negative patterns of behaviour.
Complex carbohydrates:	Unrefined, high-fibre items such as brown rice, potatoes and whole-wheat products.
Crohn's disease:	Inflammation of the gut that leads to symptoms of cramps, diarrhoea and weight loss.
Digoxin:	A cardiac glycoside used to treat heart irregularities such as heart failure and arrhythmia (a change in the rhythm or strength of the heartbeat).
Endogenous depression:	Used to refer to depression caused by genetic or biochemical predispositions. Now more often used as a term to denote the depth and severity of depression.
Fibromyalgia:	A chronic pain condition characterized by generalized muscle aches, stiffness and exhaustion.
Fight or flight response:	An involuntary response to a severely stressful stimulus involving dry mouth, nausea, urgency to empty the bowels and/or bladder, and rapid, shallow breathing.

Flower remedies:	Flower remedies can be used as a gentle, non-addictive way of treating symptoms that arise from stress, trauma or accident.
Fructose:	Fruit sugar.
Gall bladder disease:	Inflammation of the gall bladder and the presence of gall stones can cause agonizing pain and general digestive discomfort.
Holistic perspective:	An approach to healing that attempts to treat the whole person including mental, emotional and physical problems.
Homoeopathy:	The treatment of patients with highly dilute medicines which, when given to a healthy person, would produce the symptoms that the sick patient is suffering from.
Hyperthyroidism:	A condition that is produced by an over-active thyroid gland. Common symptoms include weight loss, anxiety and rise in body temperature.
Hyperventilation:	Anxious breathing that is both rapid and shallow.
Hypnotherapy:	The treatment of ill-health by the use of hypnosis (a deeply relaxed state where the client is open to acceptable suggestion). It can also be used as a psychotherapeutic tool.
Hypoglycaemia:	Low blood sugar levels that can lead to dizziness, disorientation and anxiety.
Hypothalamus:	Part of the limbic system in the brain which exerts overall control over the sympathetic nervous system.

Hypothyroidism:	An underactive thyroid gland that can lead to symptoms of lack of energy, sluggishness, chilliness, constipation and mood swings.
Iridology:	A diagnostic system based on studying the iris of the eye.
Irritable Bowel Syndrome:	A stress-related disorder of the digestive tract that can give rise to symptoms of stomach pain, abdominal bloating, excess wind and troublesome alternation between constipation and diarrhoea.
Limbic system:	A network of nerve pathways in the brain that are concerned with the expression of instincts and emotions, as well as memory.
Manic depression:	An illness that involves alternating episodes of mania and depression. In exaggerated states of euphoria a patient may also develop delusions about themselves.
ME:	Also referred to as Chronic Fatigue Syndrome. This is a debilitating condition that can arise as a result of physical and emotional burnout, or following a severe viral illness where adequate recuperation has not taken place. Symptoms include severe fatigue, mood swings, difficulty in concentrating, digestive problems and general muscular aches and pain.
Monoamine oxidase inhibitors (MAOIs):	One of the three main categories of antidepressant drugs.
Moxibustion:	This procedure can sometimes be used in combination with acupuncture and involves the burning of a cone of the herb *artemesia vulgaris*

(also called *moxa*) above the acupressure point that is being worked on.

Neurotransmitters: Chemicals that transmit impulses from nerve endings to another nerve or muscle cell.

Noradrenaline: A precursor to adrenaline.

Nutritional therapy: The treatment of illness through improving nutritional status. This can involve dietary measures alone, or may also include nutritional supplements and/or identifying food intolerances and sensitivities.

Oestrogen: One of the female sex hormones produced by the ovaries.

Osteopathy: The manipulation of the skeletal system in order to correct postural and mechanical problems.

Pancreas: The organ that secretes the hormone insulin which regulates blood sugar levels.

Pilates: A system of exercise that concentrates on low repetitions of precise, controlled movements designed to improve flexibility, muscle tone and overall shape.

Post-traumatic stress syndrome: Anxiety that follows on for an extended period of time after experiencing an extremely severe traumatic experience. Symptoms may include sleep disturbance, flashbacks, panic attacks and hyperventilation.

Progesterone: A female sex hormone whose levels rise sharply during pregnancy or during the second half of the menstrual cycle.

Psoriasis:	A skin condition which is thought to be stress-related. It is characterized by patches of thickened, scaly skin which may or may not be intensely itchy or sore. Affected areas are commonly on both knees and both elbows.
Psychoanalysis:	A method of treating emotional disorders based on the concepts of Sigmund Freud. Emphasis is put on free association, analysis of dreams, and talking about early childhood experience.
Psychoneuro-immunology:	The study of the effect of the mind and emotions on the body. Within this context of study, links have been made between enhanced immune system performance and a positive state of mind, while the reverse has also been shown to be true.
Psychotherapy:	The treatment of mental or emotional disorders by psychological means.
Refined carbohydrates:	These are ingredients that have had the fibre removed from them, such as white flour.
Reflexology:	A system of diagnosis and healing that involves applying controlled pressure to the soles of the feet.
Rheumatoid arthritis:	A painful inflammatory condition that causes swelling, stiffness and severe pain of the small joints in the fingers, toes, elbows and knees. It is classed as an auto-immune disorder. The latter involves the self-defence mechanism of the body losing the ability to distinguish between undesirable invaders, which need to be

attacked by the immune system, and benign cells of the body. As a result, the body begins to attack itself.

Saturated fat: Items which are high in saturated fat include butter, full-fat cheese and cream. When eaten in large quantities on a regular basis, these are thought to increase our vulnerability to developing diseases of the heart and circulatory system.

Seasonal Affective Disorder (SAD): Mood swings and depression which set in during the winter months as a result of reduced exposure to sunlight.

Selective serotonin re-uptake inhibitors (SSRIs): A major category of modern antidepressant medication that is known to boost serotonin levels in our systems.

Serotonin: A brain chemical (neurotransmitter) which helps regulate mood.

Shiatsu: A system of healing which applies regulated pressure on specific parts of the body.

Steroids: Compounds which include sex hormones, cortisol and adrenocortical hormones. They can be used medicinally where inflammation needs to be reduced quickly, or in the form of hormone replacement therapy in order to ease menopausal problems.

Sucrose: Refined white table sugar.

T'ai chi: A system of slow, graceful movements that is thought to calm the mind, reduce physical stress and balance energy levels.

Theophylline:	A compound that is derived from caffeine which can be used as a muscle relaxant in asthma sufferers or as a diuretic to stimulate the excretion of excess fluid from the body.
Tricyclics:	Another category of antidepressant very much in favour until the development of SSRIs.
Viral illness:	Viruses can give rise to any number of illnesses, from the common cold to chicken pox. In contrast to developments in the treatment of bacterial infections, very few specific anti-viral drugs have been developed to combat the symptoms of viral illness.
Yoga:	A system of movement and breathing which can help reduce mental and physical stress, while building up physical stamina, strength and flexibility.

Personal Health Notes